OUR ANCESTORS CAME FROM OUTER SPACE

They colonized Earth and carefully nurtured mankind.

Their advanced technology made them Gods on a primitive planet.

Even now their secret civilization monitors the progress of humanity.

Erich von Däniken and Walter Ernsting discovered the key to their hidden empire.

And were given a soul-searing message kept sealed for 20,000 years.

THE DAY THE GODS DIED

An Extraordinary New Experience
by Walter Ernsting

the day
the
gods died

walter ernsting

Translated by Wendayne Ackerman
Introduction by Erich von Däniken

THE DAY THE GODS DIED
A Bantam Book / December 1976

Originally published in Germany under the title
DER TAG, AN DEM DIE GOETTER STARBEN

All rights reserved.
Copyright © 1971 by Walter Ernsting.
Translation copyright © 1976 by Bantam Books, Inc.
This book may not be reproduced in whole or in part, by
mimeograph or any other means, without permission.
For information address: Bantam Books, Inc.

ISBN 0-553-02060-9

Published simultaneously in the United States and Canada

Bantam Books are published by Bantam Books, Inc. Its trade-
mark, consisting of the words "Bantam Books" and the por-
trayal of a bantam, is registered in the United States Patent
Office and in other countries. Marca Registrada. Bantam
Books, Inc., 666 Fifth Avenue, New York, New York 10019.

PRINTED IN THE UNITED STATES OF AMERICA

I am searching for a sign, a symbol, something like an inscription somewhere on Earth. I'll find this sign on a sphere. Once I've recognized it I'll see it again and again and everywhere. Something on this planet is calling, beckoning, and will not let me go.

As I am writing these lines I do not know what this sign looks like, but I have "seen" and felt it a hundred times.

Erich von Däniken
September 13, 1970
Regensdorf, Switzerland

Erich von Däniken
P.O. Box 3143
8105 Regensdorf
April 16, 1971

Walter Ernsting
Prinzigerstrasse 16
A-5020 Salzburg

Dear Walter,

I've just put down your manuscript. I'm enthusiastic and perplexed! Do you seriously consider having this experience published?

Actually this should be cause for unrestrained mirth, for *no editor would buy this story from you!* Thank heavens! Anyhow, nobody would believe it. And the few who understand and think . . . say, won't I have to fear having spies after me constantly on my future journeys?

This is what I suggest: keep the manuscript strictly for your own use. Circulate it amongst your friends, at most. And if you believe a publisher might print your tale, then change the important data, let Sacsayhuaman become the Gobi desert, have Professor Homet be called "Vandenberg"—a good name, always effective!—but above all, I implore you: *keep the station's location a secret!* Shift it to the Arabian desert, for all I care to the Queen of Sheba, or somewhere way up north.

Holy Moses! Just imagine our crazy world

organizing expeditions and sightseeing tours to Sacsayhuaman. I shudder to think of it! And then some day I'll really have to flee: *to another time plane*. Please, spare me that. There are a few things I have to take care of in this one here before I sign off.

Or remember to use the old excuse: ". . . any similarities between names and places are purely coincidental . . . blah-blah-blah."

Ciao! Cordially, your old friend,

Erich

author's note

I've hesitated a long time before showing this report to a publisher. My reason for this was the preceding letter, written by my friend Erich von Däniken. He was still in prison in 1971; in his cell he had the chance to read my manuscript and to make additions or deletions. He tried to discourage me. If now I have decided to make this fictionalized account available to the general public, the main reason is that reality threatens to overtake the fantastic elements of this story.

Those subterranean installations under the Andes *do exist*. This has become a matter of common knowledge today. They are even mightier and more incredible than I described them. Maybe they came to be in the manner I have described in this volume. That explanation seems logical to me. And as for the aliens' base of observation, I would not guarantee that it does *not* exist.

Our world is full of mysteries, and many of them may never be solved. Men like Jacques Bergier, Erich von Däniken, Louis Pauwels, Robert Charroux, Peter Krause, and many others only wish to prod mankind into considering things in a different light, to stimulate science and research and thus bring about a long overdue reexamination of petrified dogmas and teachings.

This is what I personally have been trying to do in my novels for the last twenty years.

And this is what I am attempting to accomplish with the present work.

Many thanks to all who helped me with this task, and particularly to Erich von Däniken, without whom this book would never have been written.

Walter Ernsting
(Clark Darlton)
Salzburg, 1974

the day
the
gods died

how it began

When they reached 4,000 meters' altitude, they had to pause. The narrow rock ledge widened to a small plateau where it was safe to stay and rest. Above, the peaks of the Andes were shrouded in clouds. Below, the rock wall dropped sheer down to the mesa.

The three explorers unpacked their provisions.

"And you really believe, Dr. A., that we'll find on that mountaintop what we hope to?" The professor rummaged in his knapsack for sausage and bread. "Dr. A., do you think we'll find what we're looking for up there?" He was sitting on a flat stone, his back leaning against the rock.

Dr. A. nodded. "There's no doubt of it. The reports are vague, sure. So far no one else had the courage to draw the right conclusions. If your way of thinking weren't like mine, you wouldn't be sitting here." He pointed up to the clouds. "It's that summit over there, I believe. Another two or three hundred meters. It's not supposed to be a proper peak, but rather a shallow depression without any gravitational pull. The only place on this plateau where the laws of nature are no longer valid . . ."

The third member of the scientific team remained

*silent. He devoted his full attention to the sausage and
bread as if pretending that this whole affair did not
concern him. He was Dr. A.'s best friend and didn't
need to waste any words.*

The professor, however, kept on.

*"You are right. If I hadn't believed you, I
wouldn't be here now, trying to breathe this thin atmosphere. The report is both vague and exact at the same
time: it's impossible to ignore it. Maybe Dr. Hendircks
was wrong—who knows? Breathing difficulties, not
enough oxygen, the sun—there are a hundred possibilities that might give rise to hallucinations. Yet, if
they weren't hallucinating—" here his voice grew
more emphatic, "—then we're on the track of a most
unique secret."*

*"Right!" said Dr. A., taking a hefty bite of his
sausage.*

*They had started out on this expedition weeks
ago. With the pigheaded zealousness of the true fanat-
ic, Dr. A. had succeeded in convincing the professor
that he was not chasing after a phantom. And not only
that! A scientific mystery, a secret, perhaps even a sensation was waiting for them to discover it.*

*It was late in the morning. The warming rays of
the sun were intermingled with the biting cold breath
of eternal snow.*

*Half an hour of rest, then they were on their way
again.*

*Once more the plateau narrowed to the thin,
rocky ledge supposedly leading up to the top of the
mountain. So far the report was correct, though Hendircks had stressed that he had seen this path only
from an airplane.*

*To their right was the vertical rock wall; to their
left, the precipice.*

*Now B. assumed the lead. The men had roped
themselves together, for a single wrong step could result in a fatal fall into the abyss. A. was in the middle,
while the professor brought up the rear.*

They had advanced a few hundred meters when

B. suddenly came to a halt. He pointed to the rock wall and turned around.

"There it is again—a bird's head with a human face! Chiseled into the rock up here. It's incredible!"

"Kind of a signpost," ventured Dr. A. "We seem to be on the right track."

B. went on, but then something very odd happened. It was their good fortune that Dr. A.'s reaction was swift and appropriate when B., who was walking ahead, suddenly and without apparent cause, jumped up into the air.

At least he appeared to leap upward, but he did not come down again right away. He remained in the air, floating sideways toward the precipice. Dr. A. braced his feet against the ground as hard as he could, waiting for the inevitable jolt. The professor also steadied himself, although he did not understand what was taking place before his very eyes.

Dr. A. felt the rope slowly grow taut. Then, suddenly, he regained his original weight. He plummeted vertically down like a stone, until his fall was stopped by the rope. The sudden violent jerk swept Dr. A. almost off his feet, but the professor held on tight, too, while B. kept swinging to and fro like a pendulum, until his two friends managed to pull him up to safety again. Directly in front of the bird's-head sculpture, B. scrambled back onto the ledge. He was pale, and his body shook all over. He sat down.

"What on earth was that? Something threw me up into the air!"

"Let's keep calm," said Dr. A., glancing at the professor. "Describe exactly what you felt when this happened."

"What I felt? I was suddenly weightless! The ground dropped away from under my feet. And as I was floating above the abyss, everything became normal again, and I began to fall."

The professor inspected the sculpture. Before anyone could hold him back, he took a step forward and grasped tightly with both hands the stony beak of the bird's head. His legs suddenly slid forward and floated up into the air. He quickly drew then back and landed again on his feet. Slowly he turned around.

"This is where it starts. The bird's head is the sign."

"A deadly trap for anyone who doesn't know about it." Dr. A. pointed toward the mountaintop. "Ten meters without any gravity, till the next signpost. I wonder how they accomplished that?"

"Who?" inquired B. "The Incas?"

Dr. A. did not reply. He knew they were on the right path. In one hour they could reach their goal. Then the tiny valley on the summit would lie before them, where Hendircks had landed with a helicopter. It had not been an easy touchdown, for there the laws of Earth's gravitational pull were different.

Hendircks's account had closed with these words:

"Who was it high up here, almost five thousand meters above sea level, who created their own world that perhaps corresponded to the conditions they were accustomed to on their lost homeland? The thin atmosphere and the greatly reduced gravity would indicate Mars. But we know that Mars did not produce any intelligent life. Another planet, then? Were they wrecked space travelers who had to spend the rest of their lives on Earth amidst primitive creatures who regarded them as gods descended from Heaven?"

This time Dr. A. was the first to step forward onto the rocky ledge.

one

This is how it all began, more than thirty-five years ago.

The preceding episode, retold in my own words, comes from a novel by P.A. Müller. I was fifteen years old when I read this novel, and the question at the end preoccupied my thoughts for the rest of my life.

This was the essential question: Were the ancient gods really astronauts from another world?

At a boarding school, I hadn't much time to think seriously about these problems, though I used to discuss them with my friends. Back in 1935, these discussions were usually dominated by another question, namely whether space travel was possible at all. Not until there was a positive answer to that question would the time be ripe to consider the possibility that, thousands of years ago, visitors from outer space, from another solar system, might have landed here on Earth.

Youth always seeks new ways. Youth is forever filled by an inner urge to oppose the status quo. In those days it would have been impossible to give release to this irresistible urge by violence—breaking chairs, making protest marches, or overturning police cars. Our solution lay in other ways: We tried to *think* in a revolutionary manner.

New thoughts are always revolutionary.

Even at that time I knew that it had not been just that novel that changed my life. I used to hear a soundless voice when I was alone, clearest at night, after I had crawled under my blankets. It was as if someone were speaking to me, asking me questions demanding a definite answer. In those days I believed that I was just talking to myself. But those lonely hours were the most rewarding I could have experienced.

Yet all this was nothing but a taste of things to come.

In that year, Palm Sunday fell on the 14th of April. Easter vacation was about to start. Since my parents had travel plans of their own, they brought me home early from my school. They left that same day on their trip. I stayed home alone with my aunt and the maid. Since we lived in a large house surrounded by a gorgeously uncultivated garden, I never felt the desire to accompany my parents on their journeys. That would not have been a real vacation for me. I loved our house and garden; I loved the precious freedom to run wild to my heart's content.

That day, the Sunday before Easter, I had a strange experience whose significance could not have been clear to me then. It is only now, when all lies behind me and I am writing down the mysterious and almost supernatural part of my life, that I can succeed in reconstructing that date.

My aunt had gone to visit a neighbor, and the maid had her day off. I was alone in the house. I was upstairs in my rooms that were crammed full of books and my old toys that I could not bear to part with. I was tired, and so I undressed, although it was still light outdoors. I picked up a book at random and lay down on my bed.

I've forgotten the title of that book, but it was a novel taking place in Egypt. Egypt, too, has always fascinated me, just like South America, Peru, and the Andes—all sites of unsolved mysteries and buildings shrouded in secrecy, especially the pyramids. The hero of that novel had discovered the entrance to an unknown pyramid and had penetrated inside. In addition to the usual treasure, he found an unbelievably well-preserved mummy and decided to reawaken it to life. Our hero proceeded, convinced that the mummy had been properly prepared and placed inside its tomb for that sole purpose.

I stopped reading and put the book aside.

Life after death . . . ?

I was convinced there must be some survival after death, but I was equally sure that it had nothing in common with church dogma. Even at the age of fifteen, I regarded religions as allegories and vague transmissions of events that actually had taken place at some time in the distant past. Besides, I had already noticed that all the old religions of this world resembled each other—as if they all had the same origin.

I was still too young then to think these thoughts through to their logical conclusion. But that evening, as I was lying on my bed mulling over what I had just read, everything suddenly became crystal clear. For a fraction of a second there was no longer any unsolved problem; all questions were answered.

It is difficult to describe that moment of perfect insight. I seemed to be falling steadily and with incredible speed, absorbing and comprehending everything, through some space filled with the sum total of the world's knowledge.

But the instant was brief, far too brief. My brain was unable to store up all these impressions so they might be properly examined later on. It all took place like a flash of lightning which has already vanished even as the eye perceives it.

But a firm conviction remained, the fact that someone had spoken to me with an audible voice, just one sentence, a short, urgent message: *Help us find the truth—it is imperative!*

Which truth? The truth of what comes after death? The origin of all religions, that mysterious event which for many thousands of years remained indelibly

imprinted in man's mind? Which truth should I seek
... in a world that seemed to be one great lie?

I did not understand anything, but the urging remained. It pursued me as far as my dreams, never letting up. I could not discuss it with anybody, for they
would not have understood me. National Socialism had
dominated the scene in Germany for two years already, the Church offering only passive resistance. My
feelings were not favorable toward the Church, but I
didn't care for the Nazis either.

This conflict of conscience paralyzed my zeal. I
realized I was still too young to do anything decisive.
But some day I would no longer be too young. Then I
would start out on my search for those who shared
my thoughts.

I was not alone, I was certain of that.

But how could I surmise that, on the exact day of
my revelation, the man was born who thirty years later
would cause a revolution in our thoughts?

Erich von X. saw the light of this world on April
14, 1935.

On Palm Sunday.

* * *

I was graduated from high school, was called to
arms as a most unwilling soldier during the Second
World War, was made a prisoner of war by the Russians, and finally returned to Germany in 1950.

Yet throughout this entire period, all through the
war and the postwar years, I never lost the inner contact with the unknown people who were searching
for the same truth as I was. There were thousands of
kilometers between us. But at night the thoughts of the
others would come to me and drive away my loneliness.
This contact gave me the courage to survive the or-
deal of war and imprisonment, and showed me the way
after I returned home. I had lost fifteen years out of my
life. I stood at the beginning and had to make a fresh
start.

I was thirty years old by then.

On the 24th of April 1950, I was released as a prisoner of war.

Ten days earlier, on April 14, I had climbed aboard a freight train in eastern Siberia, a train which carried me back to freedom.

Coincidence . . . ?

I began to lose faith in coincidences.

In the meantime, the concept of manned space travel was no longer considered quite as absurd as it had been fifteen years before. Then, a derisive grin was in order when conjecturing that man might land on the Moon. Now rockets, at least, were realities. By the same token, my idea had reached the realm of the possible; the opposite side of the same coin: once upon a time, alien astronauts could have landed here on Earth, leaving their traces behind.

Unfortunately, there was also the troublesome matter of the flying saucers, which caused some turmoil in me. On the one hand, it meant a confirmation of my heretical notions that alien intelligences existed in the universe with man. But on the other hand, there were obviously too many frauds and fakes, who misused an actual sighting or landing for their own purposes, degrading this fascinating event to the level of hoax.

Belief in UFOs—unidentified flying objects—became a religion, a new religion which promptly mingled with elements of already-existing creeds. The same old story of mankind's history repeated itself: The "new believers" turned fanatical and made themselves ridiculous. Homo sapiens still had not learned this lesson.

The thesis that we once had received visitors from outer space here on Earth must under no circumstances be presented as a serious thought: This meant immediate rejection and ridicule. There was only one possibility left to present it to the general public:

As a novel!

If I succeeded in finding a publisher, then I'd run no risk in expressing the truth the way I saw it by incorporating it in some utopian plot and elaborating upon it as I pleased. Nobody would be forced to take seriously a story contrived in such a manner, but those whom I was seeking, and who in turn were looking for me, would recognize my ploy. They would find a way to get in touch.

It took four years for my first novel to be published.

I invented the aliens, let them come to Earth and land. They encountered humans who superstitiously sank to their knees, worshipping the presumed gods.

In my second novel of this kind, I became bolder. Now robots came to our world, and they *created* man with the aid of their advanced technology and their outstanding knowledge in the field of biology.

Three or four novels of this type followed, and I was flooded by hundreds of letters from my readers. But the one letter I was waiting for never came.

Could I have been mistaken? Did those who thought like me not actually exist? Did they live only in my imagination? Why did they not contact me? Or did they not take me seriously because I was writing novels rather than scientifically based books with a solid background?

I kept on writing and waiting.

I waited another nine years. Then I met Jacques Bergier in Trieste. It was on the occasion of the first Science Fiction Film Festival in 1963. Meanwhile I had reached the age of forty-three without ever having received an answer to my questions.

No. There was *one* answer: the book *Aufbruch ins dritte Jahrtausend*. And one of its authors was Jacques Bergier. He told me he had read my novels and that many thoughts I had discussed in them coincided with his views. I bought his book, and in it found my own assumptions confirmed. Yet, the igniting spark was still missing, the right style, the enthusiastic diction, the revolutionary statement!

Louis Pauwels and Jacques Bergier merely gave hints, made implications, lost themselves too much in mystical contemplations, were in spots somewhat long-winded and too verbose. And above all, they did not shock their readers. They were too considerate and cautious.

Later on there were still more books of this type. All were denied a sweeping success.

The same fate was shared by my own works.

But then, one day, something happened that we call chance.

I visited a friend.

He lived in Switzerland.

This took place in 1965, in spring.

On the 14th of April . . .

two

I had known W.W. for eight years. On the outskirts of Zürich he had a photo shop and a large apartment where I could stay for a while.

My three-week vacation was coming to an end when W.W. suggested a drive to Graubünden. We got in his silver-gray Citroën and drove off. I had only seldom discussed with W.W. what really preoccupied my thoughts. He had other interests which I shared: swimming, snorkeling, photography, and going on vacation.

Now, however, as we were approaching Davos, I was overcome anew by that strange feeling that had been my constant companion for the past thirty years. I knew that something was imminent, that very soon some decisive event was going to take place.

W.W. pointed toward the setting sun.

"Time to look for a place to stay overnight."

"Why? Is that so difficult around here?"

Of course we'd find some hotel or inn, I was fully convinced. This was just as clear as the incomprehensible certainty that I had come to the end of a journey that had lasted thirty years. I felt a slight twinge in my stomach: an absolutely reliable sign that I was facing some decision.

Arrived in Davos, we asked the attendant at the first gas station.

"Maybe you'll find something at the Rosehill," he said. "All the other hotels are full up this time of year. Give it a try anyway."

So we tried.

Though we were overcome by immediate concern for our wallets as we saw the brightly lit building on the side of the hill, the prospect of spending the night in our car was even worse.

We were given a large room on the fourth floor, took a shower, and changed clothes. Tonight we'd live it up and eat dinner at a table with a white tablecloth, like VIPs, although we always felt more at ease sitting somewhere on the beach in front of our tent, eating beans out of a can.

The respectable looking restaurant on the ground floor was not fully occupied; some tables were still vacant.

We made our way toward a corner table and began to study the multilingual menu. W.W. nodded his head in appreciation.

"Looks good. What would you like to drink?"

"Beer!"

"And I prefer wine. Waiter, please . . ."

We ate a delicious *poulet au whiskey* with rice and mixed salad. Then I leaned back contentedly and emptied my glass. It had grown dark outside. Night had fallen over Davos.

Suddenly, that certain feeling returned; that inexplicable urging from my subconscious mind, the restlessness, and the stomachache.

That very moment I heard a voice behind me:

"Gentlemen! I hope you enjoyed your meal."

I turned around and looked up. Behind me stood a man, about thirty years of age, not too tall, slender, and wearing a dark suit. All this registered in my mind automatically—not with conscious awareness. His eyes immediately held me spellbound. I felt as though I were falling into an abyss. His glance was probing, forceful, demanding—above all, positive.

"Thank you," said W.W., "the meal was excellent."

The man in the dark suit had to be a hotel employee—perhaps the headwaiter or the manager. He was still looking at me, and I felt a calm come over me. Unabashed, I returned his glance, and then it seemed as if a spark were vibrating between us. He smiled faintly as he said:

"You registered under your own name here at the hotel, didn't you? I know your novels, Mr. Darlton. I have read all of them." He pointed to a chair beside me. "May I sit down with you for a moment?"

What author would not enjoy meeting an enthusiastic reader? I am no exception.

"Why, certainly, Mr. . . . . ?"

"Von X. Erich von X. This is my restaurant."

After I had introduced W.W. to him, he took a seat. He motioned to the waiter.

"A bottle of wine, Hans!" Then he turned once more to me. "What a great moment! I've been wanting for years to write to you, but I never made it. But that is a long story, and we'll need time for that. First of all: How did you hit on the idea of writing such novels?"

"Science fiction?" I shrugged my shoulders. "I'm interested in the future, technical progress, man in his new environment—space. It's fun to me. I'd like to return the question and ask you why you read SF?"

"For the same reasons that you write it. Whoever believes in the future must learn to understand the past and interpret it correctly."

Perplexed, I fell silent. The waiter brought the wine. Erich von X. took the bottle from his hands and poured for us. Then he gazed questioningly at me.

"Yes, the past," he repeated somewhat inpatiently. "You are intensely preoccupied with it. Frequently, your novels take place in both the past and the future simultaneously. You seem to use this combination to try to find an answer to the questions posed by the present. I'll tell you a secret." He bent forward. His voice became so low that I could hardly make out the words. But I'm certain I would have comprehended—even if he'd simply moved his lips in silence.

"I'm carrying around with me something like . . . an extraterrestrial message. I've been asked in a very strange manner to go after some kind of a truth and write about it. My book deals with the same theme as yours do. I was just nearing twenty when I was charged with this mission."

1954! The year my first novel was published!

Suddenly, I began to sense many things. Memory fragments flashed through my brain like electric discharges. Truth seemed to be just within my reach—then I was beset by doubts. Was this man sitting beside me really the one I had been seeking for thirty years? I didn't dare ask him a direct question. Yet, there was something I *had* to know.

"Pardon me, sir, when is your birthday?"

Again a flicker of amusement appeared in his alert eyes.

"April fourteenth, three weeks ago. Too bad we hadn't yet met then."

"But we did know each other already," I said, then added hastily: "You're forgetting my novels you'd read."

I knew, even before he had confirmed it, that he had been born on April 14, 1935.

The very day of the most stirring experience of my youth.

He ordered a second bottle of wine, then W.W. grew tired.

"I'm going to bed. Are you staying a little longer?" he asked me.

I threw a quick glance at von X. He nodded imperceptibly.

"Go ahead," I said. "I'll soon be up."

It turned out to become the most memorable night of my life.

* * *

He led me through the by now deserted kitchen to a back entrance which opened onto a yard. A few steps away I noticed a wooden hut illuminated by the light coming from the windows of the hotel. He unlocked the door and asked me to enter. A neon light began to glow. Its illumination fell upon a peculiar setting not at all appropriate for this well-dressed hotel manager.

Was it a storage shed? The walls were bare, the cracks stopped up with tar. One wall was entirely taken up by a writing desk. The other walls were lined with shelves filled to overflowing with books, catalogs, atlases, and file folders of many colors. It was cold. Von X. turned on a small electric heater that still managed to find a place in this crowded room.

"Could you imagine writing a best seller in here?" he asked. He pointed to the lone chair. "Please, sit down." He took a seat on a box filled with books. "This is the only spot around here where I can be alone and undisturbed." He looked at me. "And I *must* be alone, so I can hear the voices. Not real voices, you understand—telepathic messages, rather. You've so often described this in your novels, and it sounded so genuine, that one could actually believe . . . Tell me, have you invented *everything* you wrote about?"

He had mentioned the voices, the telepathic voices. And now I realized that one of these "voices" was sitting here next to me. Erich von X. had to be the man with whom I'd been in contact for these past thirty years, incredible as it might seem. I had been searching for him ever since the day he was born.

I must speak the truth to him now, even if it meant running the risk that he might consider me crazy and laugh at me. But his own "voices"—weren't they crazy, too, at least for a normal human being? Wouldn't he, too, be ridiculed if people found out?

"It's a long story," I warned him.

"We have the whole night." He took a few books from one of the shelves and pulled out a bottle of whiskey from the gap. "We can use something stimulating. Let me hear your story."

We had no glasses, and so we'd take a long swig directly from the bottle whenever we felt too cold.

And the nights were quite cool in Davos, even in May.

Von X. listened to me without interrupting. Not until I finally fell silent and glanced at him with questioning eyes did he nod and smile. There was a strange glow in his eyes, expressing not only joy but also a certain triumph, a feeling of satisfaction.

"My friend," he said slowly, almost like a lecturing professor, "I could have established contact with you ten years ago, but I did not. I wanted for you to come to *me*. That would be the only proof that a telepathic contact actually existed. You were publishing your novels, and any reader could find out your address if he wished. What would we have gained if I had come to you? Agreed, we could have begun our work much sooner, but that's all. But now we both know that the past thirty years served as a period of maturation. My book might represent the first harvest." He placed his hand on a thick manuscript stack. "Its title is *Memories of the Future*. What do you think of it?"

"Exciting. Sounds like a time-travel story."

Once more his eyes announced a new surprise. Their glow had an almost hypnotic effect on me. I sat unmoving on my chair as he replied.

"You have written many time-travel novels; you are quite familiar with the concept. Only as an imaginary tale, I know. But now that we have finally got acquainted, I'll confide to you a story. A story that I only know about, and which I have never told to anybody, not even my wife Elisabeth. But first another question: have you ever felt the lure of ancient Egypt?"

"Certainly. I never had the money to travel there. Maybe, someday—"

"Stay here till I get back," he interrupted me. "I have to get something from the hotel safe. Meanwhile, look through my manuscript."

He left me alone, sitting in a primitive wooden shack amidst books and secrets that had pursued me all my life. I sensed I was close to a revelation. What would it be like? What was it that Erich von X. was getting from the hotel safe?

I picked up a manuscript page at random and started to read:

"Eleven-thousand-year-old maps? Prehistoric airfields? Runways for the gods? Were our ancestors visited by strangers from outer space? But before attempting to properly answer such questions, it is necessary to realize clearly what our historic past consists of, and what it is based on. It is composed of indirectly obtained data. Archeological finds, ancient writings, cave drawings, legends, and so on were incorporated into a thought-system [the words "were squeezed together to form a thought-system" had been crossed out]. A respectable, interesting mosaic was the result of this jigsaw puzzle, but it evolved according to a preconceived thought-system in which the various parts could be fitted together with the adhesive sometimes too clearly evident where the pieces had been joined. And this was then the only possible explanation for what had taken place in the remote past."

I heard steps approaching, then the door opened. As von X. was closing it behind him, he grinned suspiciously. He held in his left hand a package wrapped in newspaper, and his right grasped two glasses and a bottle.

"You had a little whiff of it? Fine. Then you have some idea what I'll be facing once this is published. Please, hold the glasses. Let's drink to it first before I show you this."

With that he placed the package on the table, uncorked the bottle, and handed it to me. I poured the wine and gave him one of the glasses. He continued: "We've known each other long enough by now to consider ourselves real friends. Call me Erich."

We clinked glasses.

"And my name is Walter." I laughed.

Then he picked up the package and weighed it in his hand.

"It isn't big but it's very weighty. Perhaps you won't find too exciting what you'll get to see in a moment; I brought it with me from Egypt eleven years ago. Yes, I was in Egypt, and I went there because of an inner compulsion. Someone was calling me. It was a dream, a voice, a telepathic command—whatever you want to call it. In Cairo I stayed at the Semiramis Hotel. I sensed that I was being awaited there, but I hadn't the slightest notion by whom. I waited."

I replied with a knowing glance:

"That's the way it's been with me for thirty years. But now I've found you. What next?"

"We're just at the beginning," he said and pointed at the package. "You'll soon understand. Let me go on with my tale."

And Erich told his story . . .

Erich von X.'s Report

Cairo!

The throng of crowds reminded me of an ant heap. There was nothing of the serene peace I had hoped to find here in the Orient. I was disappointed. Not until the next day when I visited the pyramids did this feeling change. I felt the breath of the millennia, the timelessness of knowledge, a hint of the veiled truth, and the mysterious call that had brought me here.

In the late afternoon I returned to the hotel. I took a shower and changed clothes. As I was pondering what to do that evening, the house phone rang.

Who would call me here? Nobody knew me, and I hadn't yet spoken to anyone. I hesitated; then I lifted the receiver from the hook to say hello.

"This is the front desk. A gentleman would like to talk to you. Just a moment, I'll connect you . . ."

There was a click, then a somewhat trembling, old-sounding voice could be heard:

"Are you Mr. Erich von X.?"

I confirmed, feeling startled. "And who am I speaking to . . . ?"

Even as I was inquiring, I realized how silly this question was. I felt it again clearly, far more distinct than ever before: the man on the phone knew me! And I knew him! He was the one who had caused me to come to Cairo! Walter, that day I had an experience similar to yours today! I, in turn, have caused you to come here to Davos—perhaps unaware of the means by which I accomplished it—simply with my thoughts and wishes.

"Professor Marcel Thomé. I'd like to talk to you."

"I'll meet you in the bar in ten minutes. Is that all right with you?"

"It'll do for a beginning," replied the old voice, and hung up.

I pondered as I put the receiver down.

Professor Thomé! I was certain I'd heard or read the name somewhere before.

Thomé? Wasn't he the archaeologist, an air of mystery surrounding him, whose treatises about the Indians of the Amazon River had caused a sensation? I was familiar with these articles, but had not paid special attention to the author's name.

Professor Marcel Thomé!

He was here, and presumably it was he who had kept up some sort of a contact with me throughout the years, although with interruptions.

Why—of all people—with me, Walter? Why not with you? You are older than I, and back in 1954 your first novel had just appeared. But Thomé never answered these questions, and at present he has vanished without a trace.

The bar was almost empty. To the left, toward the farthest edge of the leather-covered counter, sat a young couple closely huddled together. I found a table in a niche. I felt no hunger, but I could do with a cognac. It did not take long for the waiter to bring my order.

Then Professor Thomé entered the room. I recognized him immediately—don't ask me how. I simply felt it.

He made a beeline for me.

"I'm glad you came," he said, waving off the approaching waiter. "You certainly took a long time. Were there any difficulties?"

"Difficulties? You mean with my trip? Or with the money . . . ?"

"I don't mean with your trip, Erich." He spoke with a strangely serious voice. "You received my messages all right, didn't you? I never knew the receiver—that is, you. Not even your name. I learned it for the first time half an hour ago, when I inquired after the young man who had arrived today from Europe. The fact that the person with whom I had been in telepathic communication was in the immediate vicinity, I had known through ESP. I sensed it."

"I'm familiar with that," I interjected.

He nodded.

"Yes, indeed, I know you are a very good receptor. We've been in communication long enough with each other! You'll carry on my work, won't you?"

I must have gaped at him, rather dumbfounded, for a smile flitted across his weathered features. He looked so old, but his eyes had remained young. He wore an ordinary suit, a bit rumpled and disorderly. Compared to him, I looked like a fashion plate.

"Your work? I'm not a scientist."

"Thank heavens! That would only be an obstacle in our path. Far more important is the proper mental attitude and the right feeling of what constitutes truth—and of what must be recognized as misconstrued facts. For over twenty years I've been searching for this truth, and I believe I've found it. But I cannot publicize my findings. I'm too weak, much too weak. You'll take care of that for us, won't you?"

"Publication?" I tried to remain skeptical, although inside I was almost burning up with enthusiasm. "Can there be some proof that our Earth long ago received visitors from the universe? Haven't all traces either been eradicated or partly falsified so that they no longer constitute valid evidence?"

"I'll let you have some tangible evidence, my young friend—but it's only for *you*. This will give you the strength to carry this mission through to its end.

"I've spent many years of my life in Peru. A long life, as you'll later learn. And I brought something along from there—you'll get to see it soon. This is also the reason for my visit to Egypt. Something similar must exist here, too. I'm looking for it." His eyes twinkled with amusement. "No, I won't yet reveal anything, my friend. Curb your curiosity a bit, and first let me finish my story."

I mechanically emptied my glass while trying in vain to put my thoughts in order. Peru! He'd been in Peru! I had always equated Peru with the former dwelling place of the gods. In this land they had left behind the most numerous and most distinct traces, perhaps simply because nobody had erased them.

The professor nodded his head in assent, as if he had read my thoughts.

"Correct! The high valleys of the Andes have always been sparsely populated, and tracks carved in rock last forever. Have you ever heard the name of Cuzco?"

"A town in Peru, some four hundred kilometers northeast of Lake Titicaca."

"Yes, and three hundred kilometers northeast of the plain of Nazca. You'll have to familiarize yourself with that area in the near future. Lake Titicaca, four thousand meters above sea level, was especially attractive to the alien astronauts. The highlands offered ideal living conditions for them, and that's where they established themselves. From this spot they started out on their expeditions to the other continents."

He made these statements in a casual sounding voice, just like somebody mentioning it had been raining yesterday. Although he expressed exactly what I had always believed and hoped to be true, still I was shaken that he propounded these startling facts just as a matter of course. I was tempted to protest merely in order to allow myself to become more and more convinced, but I dared not interrupt.

"About twenty years ago," he continued, "I started out from Cuzco for a hike in the mountains. I felt certain something must be up there, never before discovered by anyone. Even if someone had accidentally stumbled on them, he had not properly interpreted the signs. Or his interpretation was made to fit his long-outdated view of the world." He looked at me and smiled, just with his eyes, winking at me. "Do you know what I found?"

"The proof?"

He shook his head.

"Not direct proof, young friend. The key to the evidence. Or better: the key figure. But let me tell you my story in the order it happened. At the foot of the summit plateau—a rocky, bare mesa—I left my native companions behind me. They expressed their gratitude, for in their opinion there was something spooky going on atop this flat mountain. They might even be right, but this only confirmed what I suspected. I kept on climbing all alone. A difficult route, though I was only forty years old at that time." He sighed. "I wish I were that young again. Shortly before noon, I reached the summit plateau and was soon standing in front of a flat pyramid. I could make it out thanks only to my experienced eye. Any casual observer would have taken this hillock for a natural rise in the ground, harmless and insignificant in this rocky environment. It took a good two hours to find the entrance. I had no other choice: I crawled inside."

"Alone, without any help?"

"It wasn't as bad as it had seemed at first glance. The upper part of the pyramid was weatherworn, and wind and rain had swept away broken-off stones and rubble. This debris had accumulated in front of the entrance which, contrary to the usual custom, was situated below the steps rather than above. I removed the small rocks one by one, until I was overtaken by the sudden onset of the night. It was too late to return to my companions. They would be worried about me, but I didn't care. The entrance was cleared, and I needn't spend the night under the open sky. I prepared a meager meal from my provisions, slid into my sleeping bag, and was soon asleep. When I awoke, the sun was up outside. Stiff with cold, numb all over, I gathered up a few dried tufts of grass and lit a fire to make

some tea. That revived me. And when I had a closer
look at the entrance to the pyramid fortress, I felt unusually refreshed and enterprising. I left my sleeping
bag and my provisions on the ground. I took along
only a small knapsack with my tools and a strong flashlight.

"I advanced a few meters into the pyramid. It became pitch dark and narrow. I had to climb over some
rock slabs that had fallen from the ceiling. These
slabs were rectangular, evenly-formed layers with
smooth edges about fifteen centimeters thick. Once I
had climbed over this obstacle, the passage grew wider
and higher.

"I don't want to torture you with a too-detailed
description—you'll soon enough be able to look at
everything with your own eyes! Let me make it brief.
Side passages branched off from the main corridor, but
most ended at a smooth, seamless rock wall. Seemingly senseless, just like the roads of the Incas that start
and then come to an end in the middle of nowhere. Yet
splendid builders like the Incas could not have
created something that made no sense. The Incas'
roads were imitations of runways, and the blocking
rock walls at the end of a passage could only be cleverly constructed barriers. The secret was hidden behind them, and I had to unveil it. The only thing missing now was the *open sesame* in the right language.

"The main corridor, too, ended before such a
wall, but this time I would not consider giving up. I
knew there must be a way to open that wall. I sat down
on a large stone and studied the barrier, calculating all
the mechanical methods by which one could move a
rock wall weighing many tons while applying the least
effort. Finally, only the system of leverage combined
with natural gravity remained.

"The wall must be suspended on hidden hinges.
Once the barrier was unlocked, this rock gate would
sink into a proper-sized shaft.

"I searched for the locking mechanism—and
found it. Five meters from the wall, on the right side, I

discovered a small, unobtrusive sculpture hewn from the rock. It was partially crumbled away, but I recognized what it was supposed to represent.

"It looked like some kind of sphinx, though it differed considerably from the well-known model of the Egyptian original. Yet there was a definite resemblance. Upon closer examination with my flashlight, I noticed that the figure was not solidly connected with the wall, therefore it might be possible to move it.

"After several attempts—time and erosion had done their work—the locking mechanism began to loosen up, and the figure slid back into the wall. At the same time, the seamless, rocky barrier at the end of the corridor slowly sank down—just as I had hoped it would. The bright cone of my flashlight illuminated the chamber lying behind it.

"I stood rooted to the ground, hardly daring to breathe. I was convinced I was the first in many generations to have penetrated thus far. Before me stretched out a room, perhaps twenty by twenty meters in size, not too high, filled with the strangest objects."

He paused for a while, then motioned to the waiter and asked him for a glass of water. I used the opportunity to order another cognac. Expectantly, I hung on his lips. I asked no questions.

Thomé continued after a short interval.

"I am not easily frightened, please believe me. But some things fill me with awe. If ever some day you stand at the entrance of this chamber, you'll understand what I mean. I've gone back to it many times. Every time it is the same. I could never completely overcome the awe aroused in me by what I had found in there—and today I no longer wish to. The awesome responsibility that fate has placed on my shoulders has grown too heavy for me; I cannot bear this burden any longer. I've grown too weak for it." He looked at me. "You are young, healthy, and strong— and filled with an almost holy zeal. You will do what I did not dare to undertake for twenty years—and these years today seem to have stretched to two hundred."

He fell silent again, but this time I posed a question:

"What did you find there, Professor Thomé?"

"Your question should have been phrased differently. Not what did I find there, but rather what didn't I dare to do all these twenty years. I'll tell you what it is: *to write a book!* To report the truth! And you won't be able to do it either, without getting into undreamed-of difficulties. You can only reveal a few facts, and then in the end leave the big question open. But the entire truth . . . ?"

He resolutely shook his head. "No, my friend, you won't be able to tell it to anybody. You are the first person to be told by me, and someday you'll in turn encounter someone who may become a member of the initiated. All the others may guess at the truth throughout many decades, until it will gradually turn into certainty. It's not possible to change overnight people's outlook on life on this Earth and their view of the cosmos."

I sensed even then that he was right. Although I planned differently, Walter, things developed the way he had predicted. To this very day, I haven't accomplished anything. Nothing at all! I merely started my book—you read a few pages. But I can't finish it until I've been to South America. But let me go on with my story . . .

Thomé continued to describe the mysterious chamber he had discovered.

"Time had left its mark on the hidden room. There was evidence of destruction and decay, yet some objects had escaped the ravages of time, were well preserved, or at least in a condition to permit an educated guess as to what their original purpose had been. I found a weapon, apparently no longer in working order, evidently something like an energy gun. A laser gun, probably. Some time later I saw a similar weapon in action—which confirmed what I had then surmised. Then there were some cubes resembling machines, with crumbled edges, grown useless. Spiral-shaped pegs were dangling from the ceiling in a crazy tangle, and in the corner I noticed an egg-shaped, yellow structure.

"And then I saw the time machine!"

It took a few seconds until what he had said sank in.

A time machine—?

"Professor Thomé!"

"I didn't realize it immediately, dear Mr. von X. A cage, I thought at first, with thin metal rods that could never have been manufactured by the natives of that period. A case that could be locked, with a chair sitting inside. Next to it several devices whose purpose seemed a complete mystery for the time being. Underneath the cage was a thick slab of metal; later on I found out this was a perfectly preserved energy condenser, a storage battery with an inconceivable capacity even by modern-day standards. It could definitely not have been devised and built by our ancestors."

"On what do you base your assumption that you were dealing with a time machine?" I asked him. "That exists only in H.G. Wells's imagination!"

"I tried it out," he said simply. "It's not just a time machine, but at the same time a matter transmitter with a receiving station located in the past, more than twenty-one thousand years ago. You wonder how I can know this with such certainty, don't you? Well, be patient. You'll learn *that*, too.

"But enough for today, my friend. It's late now. Let's meet again tomorrow morning in my room, here in the hotel. About eleven, after breakfast. Will that suit you?"

I was not in the least pleased about his abrupt departure. He had overwhelmed me with a sensational revelation, and now he left me right in the middle of his story. I wouldn't be able to go to sleep, I was convinced. I would keep mulling over this unlikely-sounding account until the early hours of the morning.

He was standing before me.

"Good night, Erich. See you tomorrow morning."

He shuffled toward the exit of the bar, followed

by the disapproving glances of the waiter. The bartender paid no attention to him, and the young couple had long since departed.

I stayed for a while longer and drank another cognac.

Later that night, as I was tossing sleeplessly in my bed, I suddenly knew this day in June 1954 meant the turning point in my life! At this moment I arrived at the decision to write a book. For that was what the professor wanted me to do.

Or did he want more than that . . . ?

I thought of the time machine, or rather the time-matter transmitter.

Suddenly an insane notion flashed through my mind.

Thomé had tried it out! That's why he spoke with such assurance! He certainly must know more than any other human being, or was he simply crazy . . . ?

* * *

Erich von X. fell silent.

I discreetly cleared my throat.

"Was he crazy *indeed?*" I inquired. "Did you find out? Or can there be a time machine? I've described it often enough in my novels. In my opinion, travel to the future is possible, perhaps, by way of a time dilation in a spaceship approaching the speed of light. But a journey from the present time into the past, that's absolutely impossible! If this had ever happened, we would have been aware of it."

Erich looked at me with surprise.

"Would we really? I thought you of all people would not exclude such a development. Why shouldn't time travel be feasible? You'll have to change your way of thinking, Walter, because Professor Thomé *was* in the past! And he returned to present time safe and sound!"

I put my glass back on the table. Outside, the dark of the night was giving way to the gray of dawn. W.W. was probably lying peacefully in bed, still fast asleep. It felt cold inside the little hut; I was freezing.

Erich seemed to be unaware of the chilly morning.

"It simply can't be true!" I said finally.

"Yet it *is* true! Look what I brought along!" He picked up the parcel wrapped in newspaper and weighed it in his hand. "He gave it to me that certain morning in Cairo. It's the key to the time machine and to the past. Without it, everyone is lost, despite a successful trip through time. There's your proof, Walter! A sphinx—an allegory for eternity and timelessness."

He unwrapped the package.

"Thomé kept the figure in a metal trunk with two locks, which he opened in my presence. He claimed the little statue to be the most precious thing on earth. Key to the past and thus also to the truth. Well . . . there it is! Have a good look at it!"

He placed the object on the table beside my whiskey glass.

I was sober, completely sober.

I was absorbing every detail, everything that Erich had reported. All seemed to be so fantastic and unreal, and yet, in front of me on the table, lay something that had come directly from the past.

Was it truly a genuine proof?

Cautiously, I extended my hand and touched the stone object. It was heavy, at least two or three kilograms.

At first the statue reminded me of a dog lying with his forelegs stretched out in front of him—and this posture in particular made me think of a sphinx. Only later did I realize the various differences.

The figure measured some sixteen to seventeen centimeters and had a diameter of about ten centimeters. It was carved from one single stone, very exact and precise. I could clearly make out the claws of the mighty paws, which reminded me immediately of a panther. Also two rows of teeth in the unknown creature's mouth were easy to recognize. The head was slightly damaged, just below the right eye. A small piece was chipped off, and then had been glued back on again. Later I found out that the figure had been dropped when it had already been in Erich's possession. He had replaced the rock splinter in its original spot—a source of constant annoyance whenever he looked at it.

The animal's head was held at a slight angle to its body, seemingly without any reason. But only seemingly, for just this oblique position must have presented special difficulties to the artist, whoever he might have been. He definitely would not have undertaken this additional work without good reason. (Only later did we learn what was behind this strangely slanted posture.)

The tail, short and squat, precisely carved, formed a rectangle. It lay flat on the animal's back. I felt tempted, and touched it in order to examine the texture and smoothness of the rock. Erich, who had watched me in silence, began to chuckle.

"You guessed it, Walter. The figure was fitted snugly inside the hole in the rock wall before the barrier. Only the gap between the two front legs furnished the clue. This is the key to the key. If one of the legs should break off, the sphinx becomes useless."

"He simply took the statue along with him?"

"Yes, after he had closed again the door to the hidden chamber. I believe he has another statue like this one. During our discussion he let it slip out that this particular stone sphinx represents merely a copy of the key made at a later time after the original no longer could be found. No wonder, of course, since the gods had taken it along with them."

"Why?"

"They wanted to make sure they'd find their time machine undamaged on their return. They probably underestimated their pupils, the inhabitants of our planet. When the gods disappeared and failed to come back, a priest had a master key made, in the shape of this sphinx, in order to penetrate into the secret storage chamber. This seems to explain the disorder Thomé found in the room."

I shook my head in disbelief. I've never lacked

imagination in my novels, but what Erich was telling me now seemed incredible and improbable. It sounded too farfetched.

"I still can't believe it, Erich!" I tapped the statue's back with my index finger. "They've discovered hundreds of these figures everywhere in the world. Why should this sphinx be something special?"

"You'll soon find out," he said and glanced at his watch. "It's six o'clock. How about calling it a day —or rather a night? You'll both stay here for a few days, won't you? As my guests, of course."

"My friend has a store. But I'm sure his wife will take care of his business as long as he's away . . ."

"Let's phone her," suggested Erich. He took the stone figure and wrapped it up again. "I keep it in my safe. Let's talk about it some more tomorrow—I mean, today."

W.W. was already awake when I entered the room. He looked at me with a puzzled expression, then grunted disdainfully, mumbling something that sounded like "Drunken bum!" Then he turned over on his other side and was soon asleep again.

I, on the other hand, could not fall asleep for a long time.

Not until the maid brought in the breakfast tray and W.W. got up did I crawl under my blankets and fall asleep.

* * *

We stayed three days.

During this period, W.W. must have felt quite deserted, for I spent most of my time with Erich whenever his duties as lessee-manager of the Rosehill permitted him to absent himself. I had read his halfway-finished manuscript twice. There was still a lot missing in it. Even if he had traveled extensively throughout the world, working as a waiter or steward, he had not always had the opportunity to visit those places where he hoped to find proof for his theory. Besides, he confided, his hotel was heavily in debt. He had to build up his business. Under no circumstances could he leave now on a trip.

On the third day we were in his "den" behind the hotel kitchen. Despite the mysterious circumstances that had brought about our first personal contact, our friendship was not like a straw fire which quickly flares up and as quickly dies down. We had cautiously and slowly groped our way toward each other. We had the common bond of thinking along the same lines that united us. Still, we had to get to know each other on a personal level.

The final evidence of mutual trust was still lacking.

"Permit me to ask you a very personal question, Walter. Do you have money?"

Was he going to ask me for a loan? I knew he had bitten off more than he could chew with the lease of Rosehill Hotel. I would have surely lent him anything I could for his book. But for his hotel . . .

"Not really, Erich. I do have some savings. Why do you ask?"

"Could you afford a long trip?"

I felt relief. "A trip? You don't mean that—"

"I can't do it. It may take years before I can straighten out things here. So if you have the time and the money, you could travel to Peru instead of me and research all of our theories right on the spot. Then you could report your findings to me, and I'll finish my book."

I was thinking it over. Theoretically, it was quite possible. The science fiction series I was writing, with the help of several other authors, was doing well. If necessary, one of the writers could replace me for a month or two. No, there were no special difficulties— but still quite a few objections.

"Peru! I don't know either the country or the language. How can I communicate with the people? And how can I even locate the pyramid? I must see that!"

"Right." He took the newspaper-wrapped parcel

from a shelf. "And take this along. It's Professor Thomé's sphinx! Time machines are your specialty, after all!"

The heavy package lay in my lap, and I felt as if its burden would never again permit me to get off my chair. I would have liked best to let it fall to the ground, jump up, and then run away.

But it was too late for that. Erich's compelling glance held me in thrall.

"If ever my book becomes a success, I'll refund your expenses, I promise. And if it should fail, then at least you'll have got a trip to Peru out of it. But I'm convinced you won't make this journey in vain. Thomé did not lie, even if I never heard from him again. Something must have happened to him. Maybe he was crawling around somewhere in those ruins and was buried under a collapsing rock wall."

A fine fate to contemplate!, I thought, while clutching the package in both hands. Erich sensed my objections and tried hard to convince me that this undertaking was not dangerous at all. The mountains were not too far from the city of Cuzco, and I'd certainly find someone there to accompany me. However, only I alone could be permitted to penetrate into the labyrinth of passages in the rocks. No outsider must ever learn the secret of the hidden chamber and the time machine.

And then he added—perhaps with a definite purpose in mind:

"In case it really does exist!"

I looked at him in amazement. He had been trying for three days to convince me that such a machine actually did exist. Now, all of a sudden, was he beginning to doubt his own words? He couldn't possibly have changed his mind that fast—or did he never believe it in the first place? That might explain why he had waited fully eleven years before he confided in somebody and revealed the secret of the missing professor. On the other hand, this might also explain why he himself had not traveled to Peru over all those years.

My spirit of argumentation awakened. Now it was I who suddenly began to believe the unbelievable with firm and unshakable conviction.

"What do you mean by 'In case it really does exist'? Why should the professor have told you a lie? What good would that have done him? And don't forget his story, Erich. He went back into the past! Isn't that what he told you?"

"Yes, but without any details. He said at the time no description could replace the immediacy of a personal experience. He gave me the key, the sphinx, so I might convince myself personally. I was supposed to follow him . . ." Erich suddenly stopped in midsentence. He looked like a person who abruptly realizes the full extent of a fearful truth. He repeated slowly: "Follow him!"

I stared at him as the impact of his words gripped me.

"Do you think he meant: follow him back into time . . . ?"

Erich nodded in silent agreement.

Strange, I thought, that this explanation had not occurred to him sooner. The notion seemed quite logical, in context with a time machine.

But by now I had come to realize that Erich no longer believed in this time machine. He believed in the astronaut gods, and he seemed to assume that the idea of a time machine was more appropriate for me, even though I had only used the concept as fiction.

I placed the stone figure on the table.

"All right, Erich, I'll talk to my publisher. I'll get there. If I have to, I'll take a freighter."

"You'd lose too much time that way."

"You've already lost eleven years."

"True, but I was young." He gave me a wink. "You've lost far more, even though it wasn't entirely your fault. The main thing now is that you have made a decision. But don't lose the sphinx! It is irreplaceable. When will you two be going back home?"

He meant my friend W.W. and myself. He seemed so eager now to get rid of me! He would have preferred me to have gotten on a plane this very day in Zürich, to fly to South America.

After lunch we took our leave. As we were driving off, I could see him still standing up at the hotel for a long time, waving good-bye to us. Then the road made a sharp turn, and Erich von X. vanished from view.

But the package on the back seat remained clearly visible.

And with it an utterly mysterious but real presence.

three

As soon as the familiar sight of the Bavarian mountains came in view, I felt a lifting of the feeling of oppression that had plagued me all through the drive from Zürich to Irschenberg. I was in a state of trance most of the time. Only the impatient honking of the other drivers on the road had called me back to reality.

My landlord greeted me. "Had a nice vacation?"

Still absentminded and already halfway across the Atlantic in my thoughts, I nodded and confirmed that it had indeed been a fine vacation.

"Your wife is in Munich, staying with your friends the Prexlers," he informed me. "She has taken Roby along." Roby was our year-and-a-half-old son. "She'll be back today."

Great! That would give me time to get settled again and to write that certain letter to my publisher. I did not wish to talk to him on the phone. It was far easier for me to explain everything by letter even if I must not reveal the entire truth to him. I declined my landlord's offer of a bottle of beer. I put my suitcase in our bedroom and took out the sphinx.

I unwrapped the small figure and placed it on

the table in our living room. Then I sat down, studying it.

The stone was gray with reddish areas. On top of the strange-looking animal's vertebrae I discovered a conspicuous spot exactly in the middle of its body. It was a tiny hole barely three millimeters in size. The shape of the hole puzzled me.

A cross!

An accident? Perhaps a small piece of softer material had crumbled away, leaving a little cavity in its place. It was of no significance, in any case. Apparently, Erich had so far not noticed the cross, barely one millimeter deep. Be that as it may, I would always be able to distinguish this particular statue from among a thousand similar ones by this miniscule marking and, of course, by the mended spot beneath its right eye.

Now my attention was drawn to these strange eyes. The pupils were in the middle, surrounded by concentric circles that the artist must have carefully chiseled in the stone. Each eye looked like the sun with its inner planets, the way the solar system is often depicted in a school atlas. Naturally this did not yet permit any conclusions to be drawn, for if these astronauts ever had existed, they certainly did not come from within our solar system.

I was too lazy to turn on the light. In front of me stood the sphinx, more mysterious than ever in the reddish glow of the setting sun. It seemed to be talking to me. (Perhaps these were just Erich's urgent thought waves reaching out to me once more.) This time, however, they were not luring and calling, but rather demanding and sending me away from him. He was *ordering* me to go to Peru!

Peru!

I got up, turned on the light, and went to the bookcase for the big world atlas.

South America was a continent I had always wanted to visit someday. Peru, Lake Titicaca, the Andes, the fortresses of the Incas—I knew them all through my reading. My shelves held many books dealing with the interconnections of similar structures in various parts of our globe. I had a theory to explain these resemblances.

Peru, the country of the gods!

Here they had landed, built their bases and spaceports—then departed again from this planet. The natives, educated by their "gods," never forgot them, forever hoping for their return. And they tried to imitate the structures of those they so greatly venerated. Whatever we know today is nothing but imitations.

Yet the secret chamber was genuine!

And the time machine . . .

A car drove up in front of the house. Voices rang out, and I recognized the loud and merry tones of Harry, my friend from Munich. He and his wife had driven my wife and son home.

I wrapped up the sphinx and locked it in a special drawer in my bookcase. Then I went to greet my wife and the guests.

* * *

The months of July, August, and September went flying by. After several discussions, my publisher had given his consent to the planned journey; however, he demanded that I first finish several novels of the science fiction series in advance. This gave me a financial freedom most welcome at that time.

My wife accepted the idea that I would leave alone for the trip. She was not so much swayed by the realization of how important this undertaking was as by the needs of our little son. She could not leave him. I had told her about Erich. His name was still completely unknown (quite in contrast with today!). I had also shown her the sphinx, without revealing, however, the significance of the little stone image.

Finally, in September, I was ready to go. By the end of the month I reached Cuzco, the city high in the Andes. Erich had given me a man's address, which he in turn had received from Professor Thomé. I was supposed to call on this man, bringing greetings from his colleague. The rest would follow automatically.

The only problem was whether this man was still in Cuzco after eleven years. He might even have died in the meantime. A disheveled looking boy offered to carry my two suitcases. I repeated several times the name of the man I was looking for. Finally he understood and nodded his head. Then he ran ahead of me while I followed.

It was difficult to keep up with him. Cuzco lies high in the Andes, surrounded by mountains reaching four to five thousand meters' altitude. Breathing was labored. And my actual goal, the Inca fortress Sacsayhuaman, was several hundred meters higher still!

Jacques Ferrant lived roughly 500 meters from the football stadium in an old, decrepit looking stone house surrounded by a high wall. The boy put down my suitcases, stretched out his hand for his "sols," and ran off, while I was trying to find a way to get inside the well-fortified building. The gate was metal and was built into the thick wall. I rapped on the door but only managed to hurt my knuckles.

Then I noticed to the right of the door a bell button, placed unusually high. I had to stretch up my arm in order to reach it. Not until I had rung the bell and was waiting for the gate to be opened did I realize the meaning of a slightly protruding stone at the wall. I climbed on it, and then a tiny flap door opened in the gate. In it appeared a brown eye which examined me for a few seconds. Then the eye disappeared and made way for a mouth framed by a tangle of gray hair. From it issued a stream of incomprehensible words. Then the mouth disappeared, too, and all I could see was an ear.

That obviously meant that my turn had come. I knew that Ferrant was a Frenchman who had always been living in Peru. He was said to speak German perfectly in addition to a dozen other languages.

"A friend of Professor Thomé has asked me to come and see you, Monsieur Ferrant. You are Monsieur Ferrant, aren't you?"

"Thomé?" The tiny flap door fell shut with

lightning speed, and the heavy metal gate swung slowly open. Now I realized how heavy it actually was —at least five centimeters thick. I wondered why that should be necessary in as peaceful an area as Cuzco! Ferrant became visible in full life-size, which was quite considerable. He was wearing a simple white suit, a bit rumpled and not quite clean any more. His face was completely framed by a black-gray full beard and hair of the same color. Only his brown eyes, his nose, and his mouth remained visible. "Enter, please! Welcome to my home." His voice was loud and clear and could surely be heard all the way over to the stadium. Then he noticed my suitcases standing out in the street before the gate. At a speed that I would never have expected to find in a man his size and age, he pushed past me and jammed the fairly heavy pieces of luggage under his right and left arms. Then he closed the gate behind us. "Come inside my house, my friend!"

I introduced myself, but he merely waved his hand and said:

"Anybody could be called that!" And added with a roaring voice, "But there was only one Thomé!"

So he also seemed to know that the professor was missing. Perhaps he knew even more than that. I had my own suspicions on this point.

We were met in the entrance hall by an elderly, corpulent Indian woman. Ferrant gave her some instructions and the suitcases. She carried them upstairs and disappeared with them on the top floor. I followed her with my eyes, wondering: Are these the descendants of those people who left mankind the greatest mysteries on Earth?

Ferrant left me no time for lengthy reflections.

"It was very hot today, even up here at this altitude. You'll find your room ready in a few minutes. You can shower, change your clothes, and then keep me company at the dinner table. Then you'll have ample opportunity to tell me exactly what brings you to me. But let me warn you right away: If you are one of those nosy newspaper reporters, you'll be kicked out of my house immediately. Then you can sleep out in the open." He grinned broadly. "But you aren't one of those *paparazis,* or else Thomé wouldn't have given you my address."

I simply nodded my head. It made no sense to explain at this point the reason for my coming here. Whether I would tell him would depend on if he was one of the initiated or not. He would have to identify himself to me.

"Thank you," I said, without discussing any further the matter of being a nosy newspaper reporter. "I sure can do with a shower. And I am quite hungry. The trip was rather strenuous."

The Indian woman came down the stairs.

"I'll see you later," commented Ferrant and stalked off as if I no longer existed.

The elderly Indian woman showed me to my room and the adjoining bathroom. After that she, too, vanished.

Sometime later I sat across the table from Jacques Ferrant. We were alone. The antique furnishings of the room caught my eye. Goodness knows, I thought, where he dug those up: A wide, dark-red sofa with a round, ivory-inlaid coffee table, two beige armchairs upholstered in an Indian pattern. The lamps shed a pleasant dim light, hardly suitable for reading without severe eyestrain.

"Don't be surprised that my food is prepared in European style," said Ferrant, pointing to the various dishes on the dining table. "I've imported from Lima a refrigerator and a freezer, and thus am in the enviable position of being able to eat and drink whatever pleases me. The native cuisine does not agree with me. Not even after all this time!"

I guessed his age to be around sixty. If he had not gotten used by now to Peru, he most likely never would.

We drank a heavy, sweet wine with our spicy stew, which indeed was excellently prepared. We exchanged only polite conversation during our meal. I seemed to be getting a last respite before I was to be thrown out of the house.

Finally we retired to the round coffee table while the Indian woman cleared off the dining table. She had brought us some glasses and a bottle of Pisco with some orange juice. Ferrant offered me a black cigar.

"Now let me hear your story," he invited. "I really expected to hear another name."

"Erich von X., I presume."

He nodded expectantly.

I lit my cigar and thought a moment where it would be best to begin my tale. I sat across from a man who knew a great deal about the story. I had to find out *how much* he knew. I must not reveal too much but rather should lure him out of his reticence. This would certainly not be easy, for Ferrant appeared to be very sensitive and alert.

I explained why Erich had been unable to come in person, and why it had taken such a long time until someone had reacted at all to Professor Thomé's offer. I recounted the entire story but did not mention the time machine and the sphinx. If he knew about them, he'd certainly indicate so.

He looked at me pensively.

"Well," he said, and slowly sipped from his glass. "That's all you have to tell me? Are you sure you didn't forget something?"

I had to laugh despite myself.

"You are right, Monsieur Ferrant, to be so cautious and distrustful. I am the same way. Please give me just one clue as proof. I must know if you have been let in on the secret."

He nodded, neither glad nor angry.

"A temporal bow-wow," he stated, and this time he grinned with great amusement. "Will that do for you to start talking in earnest, finally?"

"I think so, but I'd prefer if you'd first enlighten me about your relationship to Thomé. You were more than just a mere acquaintance. Were you his friend, his confidant? He never mentioned you in his actual account."

"That is not necessary. I no longer participate in expeditions; I'm too old and lazy for that. But anybody who goes up into the mountains must be accompanied by natives, and there are no natives here who wouldn't inform me of such a trip. If you want, you might say: All roads lead to Ferrant. Yours too, but with the difference that you are bringing along a recommendation. Do you have the figure?"

"The sphinx? Yes, I do. Thomé's friend, von X., gave it to me. It is upstairs in my room. Would you like me to get it?"

"There's no hurry. I am familiar with the little statue. The sphinx is your credential for me. Later on it will be much more than that—but that's something *you* know better." He looked at me strangely before he continued: "You don't think Thomé is crazy? After all, it isn't every day one is told such a tale."

"It sounds improbable, but as a matter of principle I don't consider it impossible that a time machine might exist. There are too many legends which point to such a likelihood. You have seen it, Monsieur Ferrant, haven't you?"

He shook his head emphatically.

"No, I haven't! As I mentioned earlier, I don't go on expeditions."

"But at the time Professor Thomé discovered the time machine, you must have been still young."

He grinned again.

"You mean to say, not so fat! Correct. But nevertheless, I did not climb up high into the mountains to the ruins. Of course I have visited the fortress of Sacsayhuaman; it's practically in my backyard. But not the mountains above it where the professor has been. They are not that well-known or famous. No tourist would bother with them, and besides, there is nothing about them in the guidebooks."

"Thomé went there all alone?"

"Yes, all alone. His companions waited above the Inca fortress on the road to Pisac. Thomé returned a few days later, a bit bewildered—but nobody would have thought of considering him crazy. When he described the secret chamber to me, I would not believe him at first. Time travel and that kind of thing! But then he showed me some concrete proof which convinced me. He must indeed have been back in the past, or else he simply found a perfectly functioning energy weapon in these caves, which seems less credible."

"An energy weapon?" My interest was aroused. "Was there really some tangible evidence of it? Von X. mentioned it once."

"I have the weapon in my possession! Thomé left it to me one year ago when he started out on his last expedition, from which he never returned. Would you like to see it?"

I nodded silently to show how eagerly I accepted this offer. He got up and went to the bookcase, where I discovered among other titles Louis Pauwels and Jacques Bergier: *Le Matin des Magiciens*.

I could not see where he had hidden the object in question, but when he came back he held it in his hand, examined it once more, then placed it on the table before me. Then, finally, he sat down again.

Full of curiosity, yet with reservation, I inspected what Ferrant had designated as a weapon. Indeed there was a certain resemblance to a pistol. The butt end was slightly plumper, and the barrel a bit heavier. In general, the whole object gave the impression of being too unwieldy to be a handy weapon. Nevertheless . . .

"Yes, an energy weapon," mumbled Ferrant and refilled the glasses. The Pisco with orange juice was excellent, with a pleasantly wholesome taste. "Thomé brought it back from his first journey more than thirty years ago. It is indeed a weapon! I have tried it out. Tomorrow morning I'll show it to you."

Very cautiously I extended my hand toward the gun and, since Ferrant did not attempt to stop me, I seized the pistol butt and picked up the firearm. It was exceedingly heavy. It was made of a dull, shimmering metal with a silver-gray sheen. I could not detect a trigger, but instead I noticed a button on the left side. The butt end bore ornamental engravings which might also serve to secure one's grip on the weapon. Despite its plump form and heavy weight, the object lay comfortably and securely in my hand.

Ferrant bent forward.

"I have not yet been able to determine how to operate the safety catch, nor how to unload the weapon. Please be careful. Don't push the button—your thumb just came dangerously close to it. Have you ever heard anything about laser rays?" And as I nodded my head with a puzzled expression on my face, he continued: "*This* is a laser gun! Around twenty-three thousand years old!"

I put the pistol back on the table.

"Did I hear you right? Twenty-three thousand years? How could one ever determine its age? No organic matter contained in it, as far as I can see. The Carbon-fourteen method wouldn't work in this case, and besides . . ."

"Marcel Thomé brought it back with him," Ferrant interrupted me with a firm voice. "He ought to know. He entrusted it to me, for how could he have handed it to a world still not ready for such a powerful weapon? A world divided into nations that are forever warring with each other? How could he give it to the human race that is still busy killing each other and always looking for newer and more effective weapons of destruction?" He shook his head with emphasis, then nodded in the direction of the mysterious weapon. "No, nobody is ready for it yet—including you and me. Both of us, and your friend Erich, are at most prepared for the thought alone that the past was different than we have been taught to believe till now. But the danger of indiscriminate use is still too much, even for us!" He pointed to the laser gun, then suddenly seemed to come to a decision. "Come with me. I'll show you what can be done with it. I tried it out once some years ago. Thomé was quite angry at first, but then he said I had suggested a new idea to him with this. Maybe it will work the same way with you and bring some new insight in this affair."

He led me through several rooms until we reached a back entrance giving onto the backyard. We stepped out into the area which was surrounded by a wall. A flashlight provided sufficient light, for it had grown dark outside in the meantime. The sky above was aglitter with myriads of stars, more than I had ever seen before. Erich was right: In Peru you were closer to the stars than anywhere else on this Earth.

There was a well in the center of the backyard. Huge stone boulders formed the framework of the vertical shaft from which icy-cold air emanated. Ferrant had stopped; I could hardly make out his face, but his voice itself revealed how excited he felt. He let the light of the lamp fall on the stones.

"Well, do you notice something special here?"

I bent over so I could see better. The chunk of rock was rough and irregular. Primitive tools must have once upon a time been used to bring it to its present shape. Surely that wasn't what Ferrant wanted to show me. For that he would hardly have left his house in the dark of night. Once more I examined the stone, but this time more closely—until I found it.

It was a razor-sharp, extremely delicate fissure, straight as a ruler, that stretched diagonally from the left top to the right bottom. It was so thin that not even a fine razor blade could have been inserted there.

I slowly straightened up and glanced questioningly at Ferrant.

"Yes," he said, "your guess is correct, my friend. The energy ray is so fine, but also so powerful at the same time, that it cut the chunk of rock into two pieces without leaving any rough traces. I left it exactly this way. But if you were to take the two pieces apart, you'd note a surprising fact—something the scientists have been racking their brains over for decades, although the solution lies right in my living room on the coffee table. You know what I mean?"

"The rock wall of Sacsayhuaman?"

"That, too, but to a lesser degree. That's not mainly what I was thinking of. That wall seems to be rather an imitation, perhaps still using the technological means of the vanished gods. No, I mean the rock chambers above the fortress. You don't know them yet. They were discovered, all right, but hardly paid proper attention to. Close by is located the buried pyramid with the secret chamber discovered by Thomé. The subterranean passages were cut into the rock with the help of tools resembling this laser pistol. They cut out big cubes of rock. Later on, the unneeded material was transported to the outside and stored where it was eventually found by the native population, the ancestors of the Incas, who used these blocks to construct their fortresses. And that is the solution to how the Incas acquired their evenly-shaped building blocks."

"If these comparatively primitive fortresses and pyramids were discovered, why no concrete traces of the actual master builders? Why did we never find any technical devices that could serve as proof?"

"The explanation is quite simple: The alien astronauts—let's call them by their rightful name—left not much behind. They took along everything, and that chamber with the time machine inside must be an exception. For what reason? We could invent thousands of theories, ranging from a careless commander to mutiny. Besides, all research used to be undertaken from the viewpoint of now-outdated assumptions. They discovered meaningless things—as far as they were concerned—and evaluated them accordingly. Who knows what else is still hidden in the rocky mountains of the Andes, waiting to be discovered? Now, at least, you know how these building cubes were manufactured. Waste material, debris, that's all."

We went back to the house. As I sat down on the red sofa, my glance fell on the weapon lying on the coffee table.

"This is not, then, just a weapon but also a tool."

"Its rays have a range so far unknown to me. I am also ignorant of how deep the rays can penetrate into the rock and cut it apart. Maybe there existed still bigger pistols, or maybe this size was sufficient." He pushed my glass containing the rest of the slightly sour-tasting Pisco toward me. "You must be tired. Tomorrow is another day."

We drank to each other.

I indeed felt tired. Despite all the conveniences offered by modern civilization, the trip had been exhausting. And on my very first day in Cuzco, I was presented with a surprise that dissipated all my doubts. There was only one question which preoccupied me and would not give me any rest throughout the coming night: How was it possible to keep such a discovery as laser pistols a secret? Was it likely that history was repeating itself after a span of more than 20,000 years? How could there be something right before my eyes, 23,000 years old, that had just been discovered by the supermodern technology of the twentieth century . . . ?

Not one, but three questions at the same time.

Was there only *one* answer—or three different ones?

"Will you accompany me to the pyramid?" I asked.

"Only as far as Sacsayhuaman," he replied. "You'll easily find your way from there. I'll describe it exactly to you." He shook his head. "No, my friend, ten horses couldn't drag me up to the devil's mountain, as I call it. Maybe that's the reason why I became Thomé's friend. I never mixed in his affairs, although I felt a burning interest in them. Besides, I am superstitious."

"You've been living too long in this country."

"My parents were also superstitious, and they lived in France. That has nothing to do with it. But Thomé isn't the only one who disappeared forever up there in the mountains. I'll be surprised if you ever come back from there."

I felt a sensation of dismay sweep over me. I certainly did not intend to vanish forever. This would hardly have been Erich's plan, for he wanted to write his book. And he could do that successfully only if he believed in his cause and obtained proofs of his theory from me.

"I shall return," I said firmly and stood up. "Please don't bother, Monsieur Ferrant, I'll find my way upstairs. Your Indian lady has showed me everything, thanks."

He simply nodded and remained seated.

"The old Indian woman, my friend, is a direct descendant of Atahualpa, the ruler of the Incas who was murdered by Pizarro in the eighteenth century. At least that's what she has told me—and why should I doubt her word?" He smiled. "Good night. Sleep well."

"Good night."

A short while later I was standing at the open window in my room and looked up at the stars.

I felt homesick—homesick for the stars!

* * *

Heeding Ferrant's warning advice, I was wearing warm clothing in spite of the deep blue skies and the burning sun. I had on blue jeans, low boots, warm socks, an undershirt, and a woolen turtleneck sweater. For equipment I took a sleeping bag, camera, color films, food, and water, and a flat bottle of Scotch, all properly stashed away in my knapsack as if I were just setting out on an ordinary picnic. A lightweight alpenstock served as a walking stick.

Ferrant chauffeured me in his old, worn-out Buick as far as the plateau of the fortress. He drove along the steep, winding, dusty road, constantly honking his horn. Then we left the flat expanse of grass in front of the Inca fortress and aimed toward a long, low-lying shed. He parked and pointed with his arm up to the hill about 800 meters above us.

"Look at those fallen boulders up there."

Indeed, we seemed to be in a giant quarry. Everywhere, as far downhill as Cuzco, there were mighty boulders strewn all over in all directions, as if a mountain had exploded up there.

The terrain grew steeper and more impassable. Sacsayhuaman lay far below us, but Ferrant gave no indication yet of sending me on my way alone. Perhaps he did not trust his own description of the area, or he did not wish to burden me with unnecessarily searching around in the unfamiliar surroundings.

"Up there, those rocks, that is the actual mountaintop. But we don't have to go that far. Before that, we'll reach a small plateau with an unobtrusive looking pyramid. The rock walls behind it contain underground connections with the pyramid's labyrinth. Thomé believed these were huge defense installations—like today's air-raid shelters for atomic attacks. It is totally unexplored."

When we paused, I could make out the edge of the plateau. We were immediately below it so that the summit rocks had disappeared from our view. Sacsayhuaman was far away. Below us lay the high plateau—or so it seemed to us. In reality the fortress of Sacsayhuaman was located on a hill, but the perspective from above made it look like a flat plain.

Despite the warmer sun, I felt cold. I began to envy Erich, who was comfortably sitting at home in Davos, waiting for my report. Compared to this place, it had been downright cozy in his wooden shack.

"Aren't you afraid?" Ferrant asked me suddenly. "Have you seriously decided to try out the time machine?"

"Professor Thomé did it before me."

"But he didn't return from his last trip." Ferrant looked past me, down toward Cuzco and Sacsayhuaman. "By the way, I remember something he confided to me. I am no expert in this field, but he talked about time paradoxes which had to be avoided. I do not know exactly what he meant by that. He said if you try to travel to an era where there was no receiver it would not be possible to reach that time. He even mentioned some dates, but then he said there was no need to worry; the time machine had been set so that nothing could happen. The time span within which it was functioning was wide enough to exclude any mistakes."

I shook my head.

"I don't know what he meant by that." Erich had told me that this was not a genuine time machine, but rather a matter transmitter capable of transporting the human body and accoutrements to another period of time. A sender and a receiver, the latter located in the past. The sender was in the present time;

it remained there. But the receiver had to be set up somewhere at some time. If, therefore, one were to go *still* farther back than that, there would be no receiver. It was as simple as that! "Well, maybe I do understand after all, Monsieur Ferrant. One thing I don't know, though, is whether there is also a limit in the direction of the future. Actually the receiver, which is simultaneously the transmitter, ought to continue to exist indefinitely, shouldn't it?"

Ferrant shrugged his shoulders.

"You are asking something far too complicated for me. I don't plan to spoil my quiet old age with it. I am a simple man who likes to live in peace."

"All right, Monsieur Ferrant, I'll manage these problems by myself. You have given me a valuable clue, and I am grateful to you for it. I believe I know what Thomé meant, and I'll act accordingly. But frankly, so far I have not yet completely made up my mind to start out on the journey back into the past. I merely want to have a look at the time machine, that's all. Even after three months I still am not quite convinced it is real."

Ferrant shot a reprimanding look in my direction.

"You aren't convinced? You believe Thomé might have lied? You can't be serious!"

"Not lied, Monsieur Ferrant. But he might have fallen victim to a hallucination."

"And the energy weapon, have you forgotten that?"

I had, indeed. Yet isn't it possible nowadays, in the age of technological progress, to manufacture such a pistol? Again and again I had encountered in this respect the most amazing surprises. Particularly as a writer of science fiction novels, I would experience this almost daily. Sitting alone in my den, I would "invent" the most fantastic things, and a few weeks later, while browsing through some technical journal, the scientists were busy proving the theoretical plausibility of my "invention."

Laser beams existed. So why not a laser gun?

"Your pistol is not total proof. Maybe the material it is made of ought to be tested."

Ferrant got to his feet. He was obviously upset when I expressed improper doubts as to the veracity of "his" professor's story.

"We have to go on. Another half hour, then you will know whether Thomé told a lie or not."

Without turning around for me, he marched off. I had no other choice but to pick up my knapsack and follow him.

Grass, the hardiest plant on earth, grew wherever the ground was not just bare rock. Jagged hunks of rock jutted out of the parched soil as if they had simply sunk down into it in the course of the millennia and were now waiting to be dug up again. I noticed especially the smooth, almost polished surfaces. This is what the surface of the stone in Ferrant's backyard might have looked like, the one that he had cut with the laser beam.

We arrived at the plateau lying below the summit of the mountain. Ferrant had stopped in his tracks and pointed forward.

"That small area over there amongst the rocks— that's it. The pyramid lies underneath. Looks as if it had been simply covered up with soil and rocks some hundred or even thousand years ago. Please don't attempt to penetrate into the polished corridors. It is very dangerous."

"Come along with me, please, Monsieur Ferrant. You have accompanied me this far. Another ten minutes won't matter."

He shook his head violently.

"Never! I'm turning back!"

"Then I'll look at the passages by myself," I said angrily and walked past him.

But then I stopped and held out my hand to him. "Forgive me, Monsieur Ferrant, I was impolite. But can't you understand? You have always lived here. For you this is nothing special. I have traveled here many thousand kilometers, in order to see this. I've been sent on a mission, and I am determined to carry it out. In the end it is a task set by Professor Thomé."

"The labyrinth is not part of that mission!" Ferrant remained firm and unshaken in his conviction.

But that was exactly what interested me. Polished, Ferrant claimed. Who would have taken such trouble thousands of years ago to polish the rock walls of underground passages? That would have been an absolutely unnecessary and superfluous job. The smoothly polished surfaces could therefore only have been the result of the normal manufacturing process, and this made me think again of Ferrant's strange energy weapon.

He waved his hand impatiently.

"Go on, before it gets dark!"

"It isn't even noon yet," I answered and strode toward the small area he had pointed out to me.

* * *

One could hardly call this structure a pyramid; Professor Thomé had considerably exaggerated there. Actually, it was just a low hillock, overgrown by grass from which the smooth-fashioned boulders were protruding here and there. Since Professor Thomé's first visit, more than thirty years had gone by. But what did thirty years mean, compared to more than two hundred centuries?

I reached the evenly shaped hillock. What I saw resembled in no way the entrance to the pyramid which Erich had described according to Thomé's report. Large boulders formed a barrier, over which I would have to climb in order to reach the rectangular opening that sloped down into the ground. The entrance itself was halfway blocked by smaller stones that had rolled down from the top of the hill. Luckily none of these rocks were too large to move.

Now I began to feel a vague sensation of fear— not so much actual fright as a feeling of regret not to be able to enjoy the sun any longer just as it was gradually warming up. There was no sun in the interior of the rocks. I was also disturbed by the obvious haste with which Ferrant had taken his leave. I saw him now 200 meters down below me, and I imagined he was glad of it. Whether he was glad to be rid of me, or relieved to be physically escaping from the immediate vicinity of the secret chamber, was hard for me to decide. Perhaps a mixture of both?

"We'll meet again!" I shouted after him confidently. "Now I know how the bell to your house works. Perhaps I'll bring you another energy gun out of the time machine."

"Better not! One is all I need," he yelled back. He waved once more to me before he finally turned around again and slowly walked toward the steep slope. After he had reached it, he turned again in my direction. "Don't forget to say hello to Thomé if you meet him."

Then he disappeared.

I stood there motionless for quite a while with my knapsack on my back, resting my weight on the ice-ax. The realization gradually came to me that I was completely alone now. I could occasionally still hear Ferrant's steps whenever he was skidding across the rubble-covered ground. It was amazing how far sound was carried by the clear, thin air up here.

The summit was approximately 4,200 meters high. I took off my backpack and placed it on the grass. Then I took a long breather while I contemplated the triangular cleft between the two rock surfaces directly in front of me. That must be the main entrance.

I still hesitated to enter the dilapidated building. What actually was holding me back? It was the sun! An icy breeze wafted toward me from inside the dark passage, as though coming from a subterranean grotto. I poked around with my ice-pick beyond the entrance and met with resistance.

Then I returned to my knapsack. I sat down on a flat stone, opened a can of tuna, and ate it with a piece of bread. I washed it down with a cup of water.

For quite some time now, all sounds connected

with Ferrant had completely died down. A frightening quiet reigned in this alpine solitude. Even the buzzing of insects was missing.

I stowed away again what remained of my meal. A quick check inside my knapsack convinced me the sphinx was safely hidden at the bottom, still wrapped in my sleeping bag to protect it against damage.

Holding my backpack in my left hand and the ax in my right, I stepped into the opening in the rock.

I had advanced only a few meters when I had to turn on my flashlight. The smooth, but definitely not polished, rock walls were cold and dry. I was glad I was wearing my pullover. I also carried with me a light but well-insulating windbreaker. It did not take up much space, and it was also stashed away in my knapsack.

I let the light cone of my flashlight play toward the front of the passage, but I was unable to see the end of the corridor. Professor Thomé failed to supply Erich with an exact description; he had only emphasized that the secret room was located at the end of the main corridor. That automatically excluded any passages that might branch off the main one.

The first side passage came within twenty meters.

Though I had been most impatient at the beginning of my trip, now all of a sudden I was no longer in a hurry. I took plenty of time. The time machine had waited for 20,000 years; it would keep for one more hour. Today I realize, of course, it was my fear of making a decision which caused me to hesitate and let me welcome any delay.

I turned into the right-hand passage.

Perhaps this was the same passage Professor Thomé had once explored. In any case, it ended before a smooth, seamless rock wall that, however, in no way resembled the boulders used in the fortress of Sacsayhuaman.

When I use the word "smooth," I really do mean smooth!

The rock wall was as shiny as a mirror, like highly polished marble, almost like glass.

No. *Exactly* like glass!

* * *

I put down my knapsack and ice-ax on the ground and examined the wall. It started everywhere, like a crystal growing out of the natural, bare rock completely welded to it. Impossible to discover the tiniest crack, the minutest seam. That was probably insignificant, however. Perhaps this was really where the corridor had ended, and there was nothing else behind this polished wall but the mountain.

Passages that would mislead? Who was supposed to be deceived by them? I believed, if anything, this shifting of the passage might be caused by destruction. Suddenly I felt chilly. I picked my backpack and stick off the ground and returned to the main corridor.

I ignored side corridors and hurried my steps. It couldn't be much farther, if Erich had listened and understood correctly—and knowing Erich, I was sure he had. The echo of my steps reverberated tenfold from the walls and increased to a frightening, acoustic staccato which gradually died down in the remote darkness.

This did not contribute to calming my nerves.

There were only a few passages branching off to the left. I decided to investigate one of them. It did not end, as I had expected, before a smooth rock wall. Instead it widened to a rectangular cavern with roughly hewn walls. This cave had neither another exit nor a continuation of the corridor.

Hoping to find perhaps some sculpture or a weapon, I let the light of my lamp wander to and fro in the underground vault, but the room was empty. If ever there had been anything inside this place, it had long since been removed. Decades, centuries or thousands of years ago?

I returned to the main corridor, and it took just a few minutes until I stood in front of the barrier wall to the secret chamber.

It is hard for me to describe the emotions and sensations that were sweeping over me at this moment. To be sure, I had not yet reached my actual goal; however, nothing but a few meters separated me from it. A few meters—and the wall.

I put my backpack on the ground and walked over to the wall that barred my way. It looked exactly as Erich had described it to me. Smooth, without any seams—one solid piece of rock. I cautiously knocked against it with my ice-ax. The wall was thick and massive.

I tried to figure out whether a casual observer who happened to come this way by accident would regard this wall as the end of the passage or something more. I was thinking of the corridors that branched off to the right. It was in the direction of the "cut-glass labyrinth," as I decided to christen it.

A thought flashed through my mind. Ferrant claimed there was a connection between the pyramid's corridors and the cut-glass labyrinth. That might be correct, even if this connection consisted of nothing more than all passages leading to the labyrinth being blocked off at its border by huge, polished rock slabs. Yet the question remained: What was behind these barriers? The labyrinth, or perhaps more . . . ?

I decided to continue thinking about this problem some time later. Now I had more important things to do. Moreover, it was about time to change my flashlight batteries. My light had become noticeably weaker. Fortunately I had brought along a sufficient supply.

Five meters before the barrier wall, on the right-hand side of the corridor, I found the hole in the rock designated by Thomé and Erich, and as described by the professor.

Only the sphinx was missing.

I remembered that Thomé's description had been somewhat vague at this point. He spoke of the figure he had pushed back into the small, rectangular hole —the way, as I now realized, one would insert a key into the corresponding keyhole.

And there was something else I now suddenly

knew: There must have been many details the professor had never mentioned. For instance: How actually would the mechanism of the separating wall function? It was supposed to lower into the ground; would it remain there? And in case it should slide up and close again while I was still inside the hidden room, what would happen then? Was there also some mechanism that opened the door from the inside?

Despite the intense cold, I broke out in a sweat. Not until this very instant did it fully impress itself upon me what kind of an adventure I had let myself in for. Time machine . . . just get in . . . push a button . . . take off into the past. It sounds so simple the way it is described in the kind of novels I had written for so many years. But now I had become personally involved in such an action. And these questions concerning matters of life and death emerged even before the adventure had properly started.

Professor Thomé had managed to enter the chamber and then leave it again, safe and sound. I should at least have the same chance as he.

I rummaged in my knapsack, brought out my sphinx, and removed the wrappings. The little statue's weight provided me with a sense of security which I sorely needed now. I slowly approached the spot with the hole in the rock wall, and held the sphinx up to it.

Both figure and hole were exactly the same.

Now I also suddenly became aware of the reason the sphinx's head was at a slant. Some type of a safeguard, I assumed. Whoever wanted to insert the sphinx into the hole would have to hold it at an angle, otherwise the "key" wouldn't fit into the "keyhole."

I continued to push it in very carefully until the head disappeared. I felt a slight resistance, and gave the figure a small turn. From then on it went much easier. The barrier had been breached.

The statue's trunk disappeared slowly into the rock. Throughout this stage I encountered no obstacle till the moment I had halfway pushed in the hind legs that were carved at a slight angle. Now it became more difficult to hold the sphinx. I could, of course, simply keep on pushing the statue into the hole, but I hesitated, for Erich had emphasized repeatedly that I must never under any circumstances leave my "key" behind. I must always carry it with me.

The creature's rectangular tail, closely lying above its posterior!

I held the tail tightly between my right thumb and forefinger, while I kept gently pushing against the sphinx. I could clearly feel the last resistance which had to be overcome. There was a tiny jerk, and the figure slid all the way into the "keyhole" so that nothing but its tail remained visible. The body itself was absolutely flush with the wall; not even the most skillful fingers could have held onto it.

I heard a soft, clicking sound. Somewhere below my feet a mysterious mechanism was set in motion, an action which would result in the opening of the gate. Maybe the fully inserted sphinx closed some electrical circuit. I remembered now the tiny, cross-shaped indentation in the statue's back. Perhaps a little plug would fit into this space, the tiny cross-shaped point of a spring that had been lying and waiting for ages in the rock wall.

My train of thoughts was interrupted by a noise. Now I let go of the sphinx. The separating wall moved downward, infinitely slowly. The noise did not come from the moving wall but from underneath my feet. It reminded me of the weak repercussions of a distant earthquake. The gap between the corridor ceiling and the slowly sinking wall widened constantly. Now the wall moved downward half a centimeter per second, disappearing into the apparently firm ground. This motion could not have been effected by a cleverly worked out system of levers; I was absolutely certain of that. After all, the wall would have to be lifted upward in order to close it again, and this was impossible without using some additional source of energy. However, the mysterious people who had constructed a time machine could easily take care of such trifles.

The upper edge of the sinking wall was now at eye level. I directed the beam of my flashlight into the chamber behind it. The first things visible were two life-size figures, obviously made of stone, which seemed to stand guard to the right and left next to the almost-vanished barrier wall. They wore strange looking helmets with odd decorations and seemingly senseless protuberances. Each held his arms crossed in front of his chest, which was protected by a breastplate.

The finely chiseled faces looked human.

There were still other figures and objects in the chamber, but there was no time left to inspect them at leisure . . . for just then I discovered the time machine.

With a rattling noise, the upper edge of the wall came to rest in the floor. The vibration ceased. Cautiously, I bent down and let my flashlight shine along and across the threshold. Two lines, as thin as a hair, marked the border between the corridor and the secret chamber.

I picked my backpack and the ice-ax off the floor, but then I changed my mind. I recalled Erich's advice never to leave the sphinx behind under any circumstances. The figure was the key leading to all the mysteries. The secret room could be entered only with the sphinx—and most likely I would need it, too, if I wished to leave from there again.

I seized the statue by its tail and jerked it out of the wall. I placed it in my opened knapsack, which I clutched with my left arm and hand. In my right I held the ice-ax and my flashlight. Without much further ado I crossed the threshold and soon stood before the time machine.

This, no doubt, was it!

A thick, square slab formed the base, which contained the energy accumulator—and probably something else besides, for the cage itself was empty except for a chair and some controls. The vertical bars forming the cage were evenly rounded, without ornamentation. The rods were held together by a strong metal frame. There was no visible seam to show how rods and frame were fitted together. The entire contraption looked plain and simple, like a disused elevator cabin that had been set aside and forgotten.

I put my knapsack down again and approached the cage. The bars were shining as if they had come from the factory just hours ago. There was not a speck of dust on them. It occurred to me there might be some electrostatic charge present which constantly repelled any dust particles.

The door leading into the cage was closed. Right now I wasn't so sure whether I should open it and enter.

I was distracted by a noise. It sounded familiar; I had heard that same whirring before.

The barrier wall emerged slowly from the threshold, gliding upward with the same speed it had descended some time earlier.

With one swift leap I was out again in the corridor, back on safe ground. But then my glance fell on the knapsack I had left behind.

The sphinx!

The wall had already risen some twenty centimeters when I ran back again inside the chamber, grabbed the knapsack and took to my heels once more, back to safety. But as this was taking place I discovered—while still inside the room—the "keyhole" to the right of the steadily rising wall.

Abruptly I came to a halt. There was not much time for reflection, but I believe that during such moments of decision our brain will function a thousand times faster than normal. It was almost like that day so many years ago, the 14th of April 1935, when I was lying in my bed at night and for the fraction of a second was able to see revealed before my inner eye the secrets of the universe.

To stay in the secret room while the wall was closing shut was not at all dangerous as long as I had the sphinx. To the right of the still-rising wall, which I guessed now to be about ten centimeters thick, was the opening for the sphinx—and I had it in my possession.

A calm such as I had never known before infused me as I felt the weight of the little stone figure in my backpack. I stepped back a couple of paces, all the while watching the upward-climbing barrier, until it finally disappeared in the ceiling. Then the vibration in the hidden vaults died down completely.

I was standing in the middle of the chamber that now once more was closed off from the outside world.

With that, the first decisive step had been made. I had entrusted myself to an unknown mechanism, knowing full well that I would die a miserable death of thirst and starvation if anything went wrong. If Homet was right, then the entire installation must be over 20,000 years old. A malfunctioning of the mechanism would be nothing out of the ordinary then.

It was too late by now to regret my impulsive action. Once more I set down my backpack and examined the vehicle.

There was not a shred of doubt in my mind that this was a time machine, though it looked quite different than usually imagined. The seat, square and plain, reminded me a bit of an electric chair. Heavily insulated, bright blue electrical conduits in the form of rigid metal rods connected the chair with the controls and the thick slab underneath.

I stepped closer to study the controls.

There wasn't much to study. To the chair's right was a lever. One needn't be a magician to guess its purpose. Simply depress the lever to activate the time machine.

But how could the machine be properly adjusted? Judging by what I had learned throughout my career as a science fiction writer regarding the workings of time machines, one could change at will the time differences desired, either toward the future or the past. For this purpose a clearly visible, properly numbered scale was required: 100 years, 1,000 years, 10,000 years—and so on.

Unfortunately, I failed to discover either scale or numbers. Nothing but the lever. To the left, two glass hemispheres, evidently control lamps of different coloration. That was all.

Could Erich possibly have forgotten to pass on some information he had obtained from Professor

Thomé? After all, no normal person would sit down in a metal cage to let himself be transported into the past for an undetermined length of time.

Or was it possible such an adjustment did not exist at all?

Did the time-matter transmitter function only for a set section of time that remained unchanged? Would the time traveler arrive always at the same era regardless of whenever he began his trip? Or would he traverse always the same number of years while going back into the past?

There was only *one* way to find an answer to all these questions: by trying it out.

I sat down on a toppled-over stone statue lying near the spot where I had placed my knapsack. I positioned my flashlight so that its glow fell upon the ceiling, from where it was then reflected, bathing the entire chamber in a weak but sufficient light.

All was calm and quiet. Never before in my life had I experienced such an absolute silence. Men and their cities seemed eons removed from me as if I were the only living being in this world.

Perhaps this was true for this moment.

I felt no hunger pangs, although many hours had elapsed since my last meal. A brief glance at my watch told me that the sun must be setting now outside.

I took a drink from my whiskey bottle. The stinging liquid seemed to revive me again, but I realized at the same time how cold it was inside the secret chamber. I estimated the temperature to be about five degrees Celsius; above zero, of course. But definitely not more than that. Still, I was not shivering with cold. But I would catch a devil of a cold if I did nothing to prevent it.

I took another swig of whiskey, then packed away the bottle. I wrapped the sphinx once more in my sleeping bag, and stashed it away in my knapsack together with the whiskey. Before I'd risk the experiment, I wanted first to have a good look around the place. Of course, I had to admit to myself, this was not the only reason. What really held me back was my inner indecision about risking the big jump.

* * *

To be frank, it seems strange I should not have discovered earlier the second exit.

The professor had not mentioned a single word about it to Erich. He possibly might even have overlooked it, for it was hidden behind some big rock slabs that had become detached from the ceiling and fallen to the floor. But there was no barrier wall to form an obstacle between the exit and the secret room.

I climbed over the jumble of stone slabs and shone my flashlight inside the narrow corridor leading into the interior of the rock. One meter beyond the opening, the passage widened and the ceiling was higher, making it possible to stand comfortably upright. The floor, the walls, and the ceiling were smooth and even, like glass.

Did this passage lead to the mirror-like labyrinth? Had I discovered its underground entrance here? I knew that it was possible to advance only a few meters when coming from the surface.

I bent down and thoroughly inspected the floor, to make absolutely certain there was no mechanical separating wall waiting inside the rock to imprison forever any unauthorized visitors. I left my knapsack containing the sphinx behind—a bit carelessly, I now realize—as I penetrated farther into the corridor. I held my flashlight in my outstretched hand. The glow was reflected in many colors from the polished walls —reminding me of a prism. It felt like walking through a rainbow tunnel.

Twenty meters, then it came to an end.

Feeling bewildered and overwhelmed, I was standing before the chaos that Professor Thomé had mentioned in connection with the mirror-like labyrinth. Now I could see with my own eyes what he had meant by that. And I understood that Erich's logical deduction must have been correct.

The glass-like walls and ceilings must have been jammed together and wedged tight by some inconceivable force. Whatever this force might have been, it had not come through the rock. Apparently it had sought the path of least resistance, through the corridors, suddenly, and with horrifying strength.

Not until now had I noticed that this layer of glass covered the rock like a diaphanous skin, as if the rock had melted and congealed again at once. Only unimaginably-high temperatures could achieve such an effect.

I looked down on the ground and saw something glittering in a small depression. Water? But when I bent down it was just a small puddle of molten, then solidified glass.

I felt chilly again. I suspected what must have happened here, but I was afraid to pursue this notion fully and to its logical conclusion. I recalled the theories of Pauwels and Bergier. Both writers maintained that there had been on Earth a highly advanced civilization which had destroyed itself in an atom war many thousands of years ago. But this destruction before me must have come about in an entirely different manner.

I tried once more to bypass this obstacle, then gave up. The rocks were partially fused together. Perhaps they could have been blasted apart by explosives, but I doubted it.

Discouraged, I returned to the secret chamber. My silent hope of finding an emergency exit in this passage had been in vain. I would have to depend solely on the main corridor. Glancing quickly at the time machine, I sat down again next to my knapsack.

The time had come.

No reason to wait any longer. If the cage was really the legendary time machine—and I gradually had become convinced that this was actually the case —then there remained no other excuse for me, no justifiable subterfuges.

I got to my feet and walked a few paces to the

door grill. I searched for a lock, but found only a knob of shiny metal. It was about the right size for a fist, which led me to believe that the people who had originally constructed the time machine had humanoid hands. The door frame was closely fitted to the frame of the cage. There was nothing resembling a contact between the two frames.

Cautiously, and still full of distrust, I stretched out my right hand and touched the knob. It felt cold; it seemed to me that the cold was streaming toward me.

I pulled at the knob, and the door opened.

At the same instant the two hemispheres inside the cage lit up, one orange, the other blue.

A thought flashed through my mind: Had the machine's mechanism been activated by opening the door? Would this interrupt the barrier circuit and reestablish the energy supply for the time machine? But what would happen if I entered the cage and shut the door again behind me? Wouldn't this restore the barrier?

The only way of finding out would be to actually try it. At least, now I knew there was an energy supply for the time machine to function.

I walked back to the toppled-over stone figure to fetch my knapsack. Under no circumstances would I leave it behind. If the contraption really worked and carried me back in time, I would need food and water —and a drink of whiskey, for sure.

Cautiously, I pushed the knapsack into a corner of the cage where it would not be in my way. I considered taking my ice-ax along, but decided against it. It might hamper me. If I were indeed to encounter any human beings, then it was quite possible they would regard it as a dangerous weapon—a circumstance I definitely wanted to avoid.

I entered the cage and closed the door behind me. This time it clicked as the frame fell shut. The two little lamps kept burning, their light shining even brighter, it seemed to me. So the energy supply had not been cut off.

I sat down gingerly to think. Why were things

different this time? I was certain that the barrier would have been reactivated if I had closed the door from the outside. *What* was different now?

The answer was lying beneath me: Now that I was inside the cage, my weight was obviously pressing against the floor, and this pressure transmitted to some computer started the flow of the energy supply. It could only be this way!

Fascinated, I inspected the lever. My hand was a mere ten centimeters away from it, and I simply needed to bend forward a bit in order to touch it. The lever jutted out from a two-centimeter-wide gap in the instrument board, which actually was nothing but a very plain panel. The slot was some twenty centimeters long. Down its length on one side I became aware of a row of illuminated—and to me meaningless—symbols.

Numerals? Letters? Dates?

This introduced a new problem: Should I depress the lever only for a certain distance, or all the way down to the end of the scale? Would this determine the chronological stretch I would travel with the time machine? I cursed the fact that Thomé had not expressed himself more clearly. Erich certainly would not have failed to inform me of such vital details, for just as much depended on the successful outcome of this enterprise for him as for me.

Something seemed to force me to place my right hand on the lever.

I felt it wasn't I who now brought about the decision but something inside me. Thomé? Erich von X.? Some unknown person, now or thousands of years ago . . . ?

My hand pushed down on the lever, and to my great surprise I did not meet any resistance. The lever went past all the markings on the scale. It did not stop until it had reached the lower end of the slot.

I quickly pulled my hand back when I felt a slight vibration below me. Not unlike an elevator, I thought. Then it occurred to me that I was indeed sitting in an elevator which was supposed to transport me along the time stream, back into the past which harbored within itself all the memories of the future.

Then all began to swim before my eyes—the secret chamber, the two mute stone guardians, the cage with the still burning control lamps, the lever, my knapsack—and myself.

I was hurled into the void . . .

four

I'll probably never know how much subjective time went by.

As far as I could make out, no dematerialization of my own person took place during this strange journey. I was not quite certain whether it actually was a journey. A matter transmitter will dissolve down to the atomic level any body to be transported, and then later, once it has arrived in the receiver, reassemble it in reverse order. This procedure allows traveling through a certain distance without any loss of time.

Perhaps this was a different arrangement here. The transmitter was coupled to a time machine. Thus no distance had to be covered and nothing was moved through space. Therefore one could dispense with any dematerialization.

All the same, I lost all sense of time. I seemed to be falling rapidly, although I was sitting safely in my chair with my hands clinging tightly to its arms. This sensation reminded me again of an elevator—with broken cables! My knapsack was lying on the cabin floor and did not budge. It remained motionless even when I nudged it with my foot. The feeling of weightlessness must be therefore an illusion.

The orange-colored control lamp gradually grew dimmer, while the green light became brighter and more intense. A ghostly glow filled the cabin. I tried to throw a glance beyond the confines of the time machine, but the secret chamber had given way to thickly swirling masses of whitish fog. Impossible to penetrate it with my eyes. My original impression was reinforced: the cabin was hurling through a void.

Finally, the orange-colored light was completely extinguished, and with it the vibration ceased, too. Now the little green lamp shed a bright radiance. The whitish fog rose rapidly upward and vanished into the ceiling. Visibility around me improved, and then I could recognize clearly how much my surroundings had changed.

Was this still the dusty, halfway-collapsed room, furnished with fragments of a long-since vanished technology, the same room I had called the "secret chamber?"

The room was almost square and bathed in a mild, yellow light. It impressed me as being somewhat larger than the secret chamber. I could not detect any resemblance between the two rooms. The barrier wall was entirely missing. The cabin of the time machine was standing in the middle of the room on a pedestal.

And then I became aware of the most astonishing fact:

I was no longer in the same cabin I had entered at the beginning of my journey, neither was I sitting in the same chair.

I simply had not immediately noticed these minor differences. The small groove next to the slot for the lever was missing. The chair's upholstery looked almost brand-new, no longer dull and worn. The bare metal floor beneath my feet was devoid of a single scratch.

But my knapsack was still standing in the corner.

How had I passed from one cabin to the other? Could it have been via a matter transmission, after all, which I had failed to notice?

Before I even got out of my chair, completely

baffled, a sudden realization swept over me. Why, of course! I was still in the same cabin, but it was so new, nearly brand-new. In my own present time I had entered an age-old time machine which had been marked by frequent usage. Now, however, I was sitting in the hardly used, new time machine.

How new . . . ?

Suddenly, while I was still sitting in my chair, another question occurred to me which I answered the same instant, feeling shocked at my own response: if indeed I was sitting here in the identical time machine, then this object had to exist twice! It existed "now" as well as in my own present time. Or should there be simply nothing but this now, while my own present time did not exist in this same "now?"

I leaned forward cautiously and pushed the door open. The green light went out the moment I left the cabin. My knapsack's weight was obviously not sufficient to establish the contact. A further clue for what use this machine had been intended: It was built to transport persons.

I shut the door behind me after I had retrieved my backpack. Perhaps I had nurtured some hope in my subconscious mind that I would be awaited by colorfully dressed Inca rulers who would joyfully welcome me as a visitor from the future which they themselves were afraid to explore. In any case, I felt a bit disappointed to stand once more in an empty, dead room, even if it was considerably different from the one I had left recently.

The room was bare, without any furnishings. Its walls reminded me of those in the crystal labyrinth: smoothly polished and glass-like, glistening in all the colors of the rainbow. The floor showed a pattern of evenly shaped seams, like a parquet floor. The most perplexing sight, however, was the ceiling! A strange looking jumble of rods, spirals, prisms, and pegs protruded from it. I could make no rhyme nor reason out of this utter confusion, nor imagine what purpose it might serve.

And then I discovered the corridor.

Its entrance was located at the proper spot relative to where the time machine had originally stood—further proof that my trip into the past had been a success. The only thing I needed to find out now was how far I had traveled back in time.

I wondered why the time machine—certainly no commonplace object in the here and now—was left unprotected and without any visible guards. Was this done on purpose? Were visitors from the future expected, who should be spared any unnecessary fright upon their arrival? Was the time machine used so rarely? Or was anybody at all willing to use it?

Then I began to examine the room. I became more and more convinced that, after all, I was standing in the secret chamber. Since the dividing wall did not yet exist, these future changes would contribute to make the room appear to be much smaller.

I flung my knapsack over my shoulder and entered the passage. According to my calculations, it would lead directly into the mirror-maze labyrinth . . .

The differences between the "now" and my own present time were not so crass. I recognized a small part of the labyrinth—smoothly polished walls, which now seemed to be illuminated from within. I no longer needed my flashlight. Although I was far below the actual top of the mountain, the air was not at all stale; I even thought I detected a slight breeze.

A air-conditioning system?

Several smaller passages branched off the main corridor that led directly back to the time machine. So if I followed this passage in the opposite direction, away from the secret chamber, it should logically bring me sooner or later to the exit.

I heard some noises in the distance.

I stopped to listen. The noises came from a side passage that branched off the main corridor at a right angle. At first I thought it sounded like the howling of the wind, and presumed this side passage would lead to the outside world; but then I noticed the unnatural regularity of these sounds. Perhaps an air-conditioning system after all? But then the howling changed. It became high-pitched, almost shrill, then gradually turned into a sharp, hissing sound.

At the same time there came from the side corridor a hot blast of air which enveloped me like a cloud. Immediately, however, some ventilators went into action—or that's what it sounded like—which removed the excessively hot air.

Did all this come about without any people? Was the mirror-like labyrinth an automatically functioning installation whose purpose was not yet recognizable to me? So far I had no idea, but I was determined to find out.

I continued on my way.

Suddenly the corridor ended in a hall. Unlike any shape I had so far observed in my wanderings, this one was oval-shaped. Several other corridors also ended in this room, which seemed to serve as some kind of a distribution center.

I was faced with a difficult decision: Which way should I go to reach the exit?

There was a metal box in the middle of the room. It reminded me of a coffin, but it was considerably bigger and higher. Its sides were smooth and even, except for the top lid, at about eye level, which was covered by ornaments and decorations. Were these perhaps some unknown instruments and control scales?

This time, too, I received no answer to my question, for there was not enough time for me to ponder the problem or to carry out a closer inspection of the metal coffin.

From behind me came a sound resembling the humming of a swarm of bees.

Strange! Up to this point I had not encountered any living being, although the time machine as well as the subterranean labyrinth had to have been devised and constructed by some intelligent creatures.

The howling and whistling emanating from the side passages had scarcely been able to frighten me. Nor the sudden starting of the ventilators. Not even the smoothly working time machine had caused any real upset in me.

But I was definitely disturbed by the unsettling humming noise behind me, which was inexorably coming closer.

All of a sudden, I was no longer alone.

I slowly turned around, and I am unable to tell to this day what I hoped or feared to see. I had not the slightest inkling how far back I had gone into the past, for not even Erich had known with certainty what time-spans could be bridged with the time machine.

In any case, one thing was now clear to me: If the labyrinth had indeed been destroyed by some atomic attack, I must have arrived in an era *preceding* this catastrophe. And according to Erich, this attack took place at least 20,000 years in the past.

The humming grew louder. It came from one of the passages and sounded oddly mechanical and monotonous. It had to be something, I estimated, that at any moment would enter the oval hall.

Suddenly, there was a scratching noise as if someone were scraping a knife across a metal surface.

And then I saw them . . .

They came rolling out of the corridor opposite me —two silvery spheres about a meter across! I was so startled that I did not budge until the two big silver balls had halted on either side of me. The humming had ceased, but instead I now heard a smacking sound and suddenly felt something touching me. The round object to my left had extended a tentacle which began to grope and explore all over my body. The sphere to my right began to hum again, rolling all over my knapsack, at the same time enveloping it with a silvery net which reminded me of a spider spinning a web.

Robots! Technical creations of utmost perfection!

I hardly dared breathe; I remained absolutely still and submitted to this examination. Any wrong move on my part might be interpreted by the machines as a hostile act. I had no idea what kind of weapon systems these sinister spheres might have at their disposal.

I obviously passed inspection, as the tentacle withdrew from my body and snapped back inside the glove.

My knapsack rose mysteriously from the floor

without anything touching it, then started to float about ten centimeters above the right silver sphere.

Then the sphere rolled a few meters across the oval hall toward the exit from which it had originally emerged—my knapsack all the while hovering like a plump halo above the globe. And now the other sphere started to hum and placed itself immediately behind me.

Somehow, these strange objects were able to *see* me; there could be no doubt about it . . .

I was supposed to follow the first sphere with the knapsack! And indeed, as soon as I took a few steps in its direction, the first sphere rolled down the passage, the other sphere following obediently behind me like a silent little puppy.

Naturally, I had no intention of taking flight for, after all, I had come here to establish contact with the people living in this era. Moreover, these silver balls would be much faster than I could ever hope to be. So, without resistance, I kept marching behind a sphere, my flying backpack trailing from behind by another sphere with harbored tentacles inside its body —I knew at least that much about it.

They led me farther down the passage from whence they had come. My footsteps reverberated from the walls, and I was accompanied all the way by the humming sound of the spheres. I have never been especially known for my heroic qualities, displaying courage only when there is no other way out. That was exactly the case now. There was simply no other alternative left to me but to act calm and confident, at least as far as my own inner frame of mind was concerned. The robots were certainly indifferent to my emotional state.

The manner in which the two robots proceeded demonstrated clearly to me that they were either capable of independent thought and action, or were directed by remote control by someone who kept us under constant surveillance. This person was intelligent and had to realize that I was accompanying the two robots of my own free will. This person also had to know that I was no barbarian. He would like to find out where I'd come from—and from when. In turn, I would like to pose a few questions—provided, of course, that we could communicate with each other.

After a slight curve in the corridor, I perceived daylight a long way ahead of us.

Outside, the sun was shining so brightly that I was forced to close my eyes once I emerged into the open. Now the spheres were glittering like polished platinum. They remained close to my sides as we walked on. At first I blinked my eyes, then I became used to the blinding glare of the sun.

I stopped involuntarily and froze, the moment I saw the palace!

It rose, undoubtedly, on an artificially created hill. It was built in the shape of a pyramid with extremely obtuse angles. The structure radiated an air of sobriety and functionality. It was a square formed by smooth walls, nearly thirty meters high, with long rows of evenly spaced, trapezoid windows, battlements, and massive corner towers.

Nevertheless: a palace!

On the frontal side I could see a broad, stone stairway leading up to the portal. The resemblance to the Mayan pyramids of the sun was unmistakable. No doubt the Incas had acquired their knowledge from their unknown ancestors—and this knowledge had been passed on from the Incas to the Mayans.

I resumed walking when one of the spheres started to roll ahead once more. I crossed the plateau and advanced toward the portal stairs.

A swift glance around convinced me that my journey into the past had not resulted in any geographical changes. The mountain near Sacsayhuaman was clearly recognizable, although it appeared to be somewhat higher. I was now on the other side of the fortress and the pyramid. The peaks of the Andes were therefore unknown to me and offered no clue.

After we had arrived at the foot of the portal stairs, my robot companions stopped. I confess this was not to be viewed as a token of confidence, for there were already two other twin spheres waiting for me at the top of the stairs, ready to receive me. I guessed this stairway to consist of roughly fifty steps, which equaled the height of the palace base. Time enough, therefore, to throw a glance at the crystal-like labyrinth whose half-destroyed entrances on the other side were the only thing I knew by description.

Till this moment I had not noticed the busy crowd on the lower plateau, directly below the rocky peak of the actual "Falcon Hill." I could make out some machines, but due to the distance it was impossible to determine what their purpose might be. The machines were run by human beings who in turn directed untiring robots and surveyed the work. I was unable to recognize what the people's faces looked like. They wore uniform clothing—wide pants, close-fitting jackets, belts, and short boots. The robots glittered like pearls in the light of the early afternoon sun.

My new guards looked identical to those that had discovered me earlier and brought me to this spot. They awaited me in silence, then flanked me from either side. We walked past huge pillars to enter the interior courtyard of the palace.

On second thought, the term "palace" did not properly fit, but I could not come up with a better designation until I was standing inside the interior courtyard. The four frontal walls formed a bulwark against the outside world, creating an illusion to those within of being suddenly isolated from everything that existed on the other side. Rows of windows and balustrades relieved somewhat the impression of severity gained upon first sight, especially if the outer walls had been viewed before the rest of the structure.

In the center of the yard stood a gigantic cube almost as large as a one-story home. It had no windows. And there was something on the roof which looked familiar:

A rotating radar antenna!

That meant there was airplane traffic here, or at least that intensive observations of the sky, or even surveillance of space, was taking place.

I had no time left to recover from that surprising discovery.

From one of the numerous entrances several persons emerged. They were dressed like the workers I had earlier seen from a distance. Their sharp-cut features and suntanned faces reminded me of the classical pictures of the Inca rulers I had seen printed in my own present time. The direct descendants of the mysterious mountain dwellers showed hardly any resemblance to their proud forefathers.

One of the men addressed me in an unfamiliar-sounding language. At the same time he held a shining golden ring directly in front of his mouth. What ensued was at first quite perplexing. The two robots made an about-face and rolled back to the portal. Almost simultaneously, my knapsack whizzed up the stairs of its own volition and landed gently at my feet! This must be a type of command transmitter tuned to the robots' receivers, I realized. These people were directing their robots via radio signals!

The man who had sent away the robots motioned me to come closer to him. The expression in his eyes was unmistakable: searching and urging. I was overcome by a feeling that he expected some explanation from me. His companions had formed a semicircle around me, but certainly not because they wished to foil any attempt at flight on my part. They knew that I could have tried to flee sooner if I had really wanted to.

Suddenly, a thought occurred to me.

Slowly, trying to avoid arousing any unnecessary suspicions, I picked my knapsack off the ground and began gingerly to untie the laces. As I put my hand inside the opened knapsack, the surrounding spectators recoiled a few steps. One man's hand moved swiftly to his belt.

I abruptly ceased moving as I recognized the object fastened in his belt: It was the same energy pistol I had seen in Jacques Ferrant's house and that I had held in my own hand. Now there was no doubt of the use for which it was intended!

I tried to smile and shook my head. Maybe they'd understand that. If they knew I'd come from the far future, then their suspicions were understandable. But on the other hand, I had gained the impression that they were expecting such a visitor.

The man let go of his weapon. He did not smile. But at least he appeared to have overcome his distrust.

I grabbed my sleeping bag with the sphinx and pulled the package out of my knapsack. I placed it carefully on the tiled floor of the courtyard and unwrapped it.

Then the sphinx was lying on my sleeping bag, bathed in the bright light of the sun and once again back in its own time era—*if* it was the original one.

The sight of the sphinx had its desired effect.

The men's attitude toward me changed abruptly. They hadn't been really unfriendly; now they became actively obliging. The man with the command transmitter gestured that I was to wrap up my stone figure again and put it back into my knapsack. Then he spoke a few words into his gold-circled device. He received a reply in the same incomprehensible language.

They led me past the radar antenna through a tall doorway into the building. It didn't look like a palace to me any more. Clearly it was a control center, or an office for architectural and construction works, in charge of making the glass-polished labyrinth in the mountainside livable. I recalled one of Erich's remarks. He suspected that this labyrinth had been a gigantic fortress where it was possible to survive even an atomic holocaust.

Did the people living here expect such an atomic attack?

And if so—who was the enemy?

Who in this remote day and age could be stronger and mightier than those who had built a time machine?

Floor, walls, and ceilings inside the building consisted of absolutely uniform tiles, each about a quarter of a meter square. They all looked as though they were cast from the same mold, and their shiny, glazed surfaces reminded me of the labyrinth's smooth walls.

By now all but one of my companions had disappeared. He was the man with the command transmitter. I tried to ask him a question, speaking slowly and clearly in the crazy hope he might understand me.

But he shook his head and made a grimace as if to say: "Sorry, my friend."

He shook his head, though! He knew this gesture!

As we were walking along the corridor, a door suddenly opened to our right. A man came out, saw us—and shut the door again unusually fast.

But not fast enough. I'd managed a swift glance into the room behind the door. What I had seen nearly took my breath away: a hall with long rows of tables on which television monitors had been placed. The room was kept in semidarkness, but I could clearly make out the operators seated at these tables, their hands manipulating the instruments of the control boards. The opposite wall seemed to be a giant, oval-shaped viewing screen. Although it was not lit up, I could have sworn it was a TV screen. I had seen too many telecasts from the space center in Houston not to recognize this!

Now the significance of the radar antenna in the courtyard became quite clear to me.

My companion noticed the confusion that unexpected sight had caused in me and looked a little worried. I had come to a conclusion about him. His deportment clearly indicated that he had no power of final decision, even though he appeared to exert a certain influence. In my own present time, I could easily have defined his rank: an adjutant.

We came to a halt in front of an elevator shaft. I had time to get a brief look at it before getting in. Inside the shaft there was a free-floating metal plate. That was all. There was no visible support, no ropes nor any columns to hold up the platform from below. Neither was there a cabin like I have always seen in our elevators. Only the free-floating metal slab, the smooth walls of the shaft—and the adjutant, who invited me with a friendly gesture to follow him.

A few seconds later we were gliding upward. I counted twelve stories until we arrived at our destination, the top floor of the palace on the high plateau.

I was forced to close my eyes as we stepped out into the corridor. The sun was shining directly in my face because the hallway's ceiling was transparent. It was made of thick, absolutely unbreakable polished glass. The walls up here were not as high as on the ground floor, so the ceiling was closer to our heads. I could recognize the mountain peaks of the Andes, but not the plateau and the entrance to the labyrinth.

The heat felt good. I wanted to take off my sweater, but we seemed almost at our destination.

At a door at the end of the hallway the adjutant stopped, raised his arm, and spoke a few words into the circular communication device, which reminded me of a heavy signet ring. A voice answered, giving instructions. The adjutant nodded briefly to me, then simply walked away and left me standing there.

While I was still staring after him, the door opened.

To avoid misunderstandings, I would like to give a title from the very beginning to the second person I encountered here. The man I was dealing with now, I immediately called the "commander."

This conjecture, too, was to be confirmed in the due course of events.

Inside the room, a man was sitting behind a semicircular, massive table crowded with instruments of all kinds. He wore the same uniform as the other people I had encountered so far, simple and unadorned, without any sign of high position. Badges of rank seemed to be unknown, or else people did not care to wear them.

He motioned to me.

I entered the room, and the door closed behind me.

Here I was, standing rather helpless and a bit forlorn before the representative of a civilization which was at least on a par with ours—apart from the time machine, the laser gun, and the robots, of course.

They had radar and radio, probably also rockets. Unfortunately, they also had enemies, it seemed, that were a source of great concern to them.

The commander indicated a chair standing before the table: a perfectly normal looking chair with four legs, an upholstered seat, and a curved back.

I removed my knapsack from my shoulder and placed it on the thick, soft carpet, of a pink, manmade fiber.

The commander shook his head—another familiar gesture—and pointed to my knapsack. I knew at once what he wanted.

My passport!

So I opened my luggage once again, pulled out the stone figure wrapped in my sleeping bag, and placed it on the table before the commander. Only then did I sit down, waiting for what would happen next.

The commander eagerly contemplated the sphinx. I could not fully understand why he devoted such close attention to the little figure. If indeed it represented a token of indentification, it was unable to supply any information about me. *Anybody* could have it in his possession. How could the commander be certain that I wasn't an imposter—despite the fact that I had shown him the sphinx?

He picked up the statue and examined it. I thought I detected disapproval in his eyes when he discovered the damaged area below the figure's eyes.

Calmly he put the sphinx back on the table, then gazed at me for a long time.

I would soon know if we were to communicate with each other. And how.

The commander opened a drawer of his writing desk and pulled out a folder which he placed on the table top. He opened it and took out something resembling a photograph.

Yes, it *was* a photograph!

He handed it to me across the table, watching for my reaction.

Erich had supplied me only with a very vague description of Professor Thomé, but a brief glance at the photo sufficed to assure me that I was looking at the old gentleman's picture. Then I realized that I was holding a truly three-dimensional picture in my hand. It was in color, so flawless that I was absolutely amazed by its perfection. Thomé's photo did not merely create an illusion of three dimensions, it was actually a plastic work of art, with such tremendous power of expression that it was like being confronted by the professor in person.

I nodded my head and gave the picture back to the commander. He seemed to be satisfied. I had recognized the professor—the man who had taken the little sphinx with him when he traveled into the future. I had returned with the statue, and therefore had come with his approval. With that, I had overcome the first hurdle.

What happened next, however, had nothing to do with Thomé—or me.

One of the instruments on the table began to hum softly. The commander depressed a button which was hidden from my view; the humming sound stopped and a square screen lit up on the wall over to one side.

A voice spoke. I looked in fascination at the screen on which wavy patterns in all the colors of the rainbow had begun to appear. The lines condensed and took on shapes, at first weak and indistinct. Then, gradually, a sharply focused and three-dimensional image could be seen.

I recognized the main entrance to the labyrinth. Transport vehicles were lined up in long rows to be loaded by square chunks of rock, which were brought in endless columns from the mountain's interior. I supposed this was waste material from the excavation of the underground passageways.

These heavy rock cubes, weighing at least a ton, were moved about by a force-field generator. An antenna not unlike radar was aligned with the entrance to the labyrinth. Robots, who seemed to be equipped with a special protective device to eliminate the anti-grav, moved these heavy blocks of stone with their little fingers, so to speak. They simply pointed the rocks in the desired direction, and then took care that the chunks kept floating close to the ground but did not leave the range of the rays which rendered them weightless.

One of the robots seemed to be defective. As the camera moved a bit, the force-field generator disappeared from view. A powerful zoom-lens magnified a section of the image, showing a huge rock with a dead man lying underneath, obviously crushed by the enormous weight. I guessed what must have happened there. One of the weightless blocks seemed to have escaped from the antigrav beams, and to have fallen to the ground.

The commander interrupted the commentator and asked several questions. A prompt reply was given to each. Then followed two brief, curt commands, and the screen went dark again.

The commander looked at me and gestured with his right hand as if to say: such things will happen occasionally.

Once more he picked up the sphinx from the table before him, inspected it again thoroughly, then returned it to me. He pointed to my knapsack. There was no mistaking what this gesture meant: I wrapped up the little statue and hid it in my luggage.

The commander stood up, a sign for me to do likewise. He pushed a button attached to the corner of the tabletop. A few moments later the door opened. My adjutant was waiting outside to escort me away.

I had not the faintest idea what they planned to do with me. I had found out that they knew the professor, but where was he? In another era? He would have been a tremendous help to me for he had told Erich, he understood their language.

I did not understand a single word.

The adjutant greeted me with a friendly smile as I stepped out on the sunlight-flooded corridor. With a slight bow he invited me to follow him once again. As I expected, we returned to the elevator which brought us downstairs.

We arrived at the ground floor, but we did not stop. The platform kept descending.

I put my knapsack down again—I had picked it off the floor as we were nearing the ground level—and looked at my adjutant with a questioning expression in my eyes. He kept smiling and gave me a brief nod of encouragement. His glance indicated that I was in for more surprises.

I estimated that the antigrav platform was sinking at least thirty meters farther down into the solid, rocky ground before we came to a halt. The adjutant led the way down a corridor which was also brightly lit, but not by the sun. The artificial light came from inside the walls just like in the labyrinth, but the light was much stronger. From somewhere came the roar of heavy machinery, perhaps power plants or generators. My conviction grew more and more that I was now in the headquarters of the strangers who, according to my friend Erich's opinion, had come from the stars. Erich wasn't the first person to make such bold assertions. My own old ideas on the subject found confirmation here.

These people were definitely not Incas!

Many side passages branched off the corridor, and the farther we advanced, the fainter grew the roaring of the machines. Finally, they could not be heard any longer. Only the gentle vibration beneath our feet remained. While we kept on walking, I noted that the corridor's ceiling and walls consisted of the same material I had seen in the labyrinth: smoothly polished rock whose surface had turned to glass. The floor however was covered with an artificial fiber carpet which muffled our steps, emphasizing all the more the almost total silence down here.

What was our destination?

I was soon to find out.

* * *

We stood before a door. The adjutant pushed a yellow button on the right side of the door frame; the door opened.

I have rarely seen a more comfortably appointed apartment. As the door swung open, a mild, yellowish light came on automatically. In the background I noticed a wide, covered couch with colorfully embroidered cloth—reminding me immediately of Inca patterns. To the left a writing desk, armchairs, built-in shelves, some kind of a television set—with a little rail in front containing a few marble-like objects. In the right corner I caught sight of the entrance to the bathroom, whose door was slightly ajar.

I entered the room and put my knapsack on the floor, carpeted with the same pink, artificial fiber. I hoped I wouldn't have to spend the rest of my life here, but right now my accommodations seemed very satisfactory. I was honestly tired, and a few hours of sleep would do me a lot of good. The thought of having stashed away some food, water, and whiskey in my backpack coaxed a smile to my face.

My hosts wouldn't let me starve, nor die of thirst; I was certain of that.

My adjutant left without farewell, and the door closed automatically behind him.

It has always been my custom to thoroughly inspect any hotel room before I make myself at home in it. I simply do not feel at ease unless I've performed this ritual. So I made the rounds of my new quarters as usual.

The bathtub was circular, about two meters across, almost like a miniature swimming pool. I tried out the water plug, a flat elevation in the middle of the tub. Two tilted faucets attached to the edge provided a supply of hot and cold water. It seemed pleasant, and so I let the water run to fill the tub. Besides, I felt in need of a warm bath.

While I was soaking in the hot, sudsy water, I reviewed in my mind's eye the events of the recent past. There were a few items that did not fit into the mosaic of my thoughts.

Who were these strangers? Definitely not Incas, who under no circumstances seemed to have been capable of producing such refined technical products as I had witnessed here. Nevertheless, there was a certain similarity—at least in their external appearance—between the strangers and the Incas. But assuming—I continued my thoughts—my hosts were visitors from the outside universe, why should they so much resemble *human beings?* Not only in their outer appearance, their behavior, and facial expressions, but also like modern man with his technical installations.

Yes, this realization disturbed me most!

To assume that life on far distant planets could bring forth only human forms and ways of thinking had always seemed absurd to me. Who then were these aliens? Why was I now soaking in the bathtub of an apartment that, apart from a few details, could just as well have been in a hotel of the twentieth century?

Still puzzled, I stepped out of the water and dried myself with towels my hosts had supplied.

I put on my shorts and sat down in front of the television set. I depressed one of the small levers at random. Nothing happened.

I stared at the rail containing the small green spheres. They measured about two centimeters across, and then I noticed a jumble of tiny grooves on their surface.

Grooves . . . ?

I suddenly remembered IBM typewriters with their floating typeface "golfballs." Could these little spheres be some kind of a film that had to be inserted somewhere in this television set? I examined the instrument and indeed found a green bolt to which I fastened one of the small balls. The rest followed automatically.

I don't know what I had actually expected. It was not out of the way to assume that the strangers wished to tell me something, perhaps their own history, their past. This room had been prepared beforehand, and certainly not during the short time I was living now in "their" time. Maybe the professor had a hand in this?

The TV screen lit up. I saw a three-dimensional color picture of an almost tropical landscape, with entirely unfamiliar vegetation, the shores of a copper-red ocean, giant mountain ranges in the background, and in the sky—

And in the sky: two suns!

I hope, dear reader, that you'll permit me to introduce at this point a remark of an entirely personal nature. If you have followed my story attentively so far, you can't deny that the thought of extraterrestrial intelligences landing on our Earth was not totally unfamiliar to me. I sought and found persons who shared my point of view. I undertook a journey into the past with a time machine.

Nothing could *shock* me, even though I was amazed by many things.

But the sight of two suns over this alien landscape—!

I felt a thrill coursing through me.

These were concrete proof!

The camera panned across the land until it filmed from above the ocean in the direction toward the countryside. I saw a giant clearing in the forest near the ocean shore, and on this clearing stood—towering above everything else—an incredibly huge metal spider on eight slightly curved legs! A spider? This first impression was quickly dispelled, though, as soon as I noticed humanoid creatures who, like ants in an ant heap, were busily scurrying around the spaceship.

My spider was a spaceship! Evidently still under construction.

The way these humanoid creatures were dressed seemed quite familiar. Of course! The wide trousers, tight jackets, short boots, broad belts—my hosts had hardly changed in their appearance since that time when this film was taken! They were busily constructing the spider-like spaceship. Throngs of robots of various types assisted their masters in this task.

The two suns—far apart in the sky—cast peculiar shadows. My visual perception ability was greatly taxed as I was trying not to confuse the constantly changing shadows with the construction work and the surrounding vegetation.

The camera zoomed in closer to the scene, and

details became clearly visible. They showed that this spaceship was not a new one about to be completed. Parts of its hull had been damaged and were now being repaired. The metal body glistened as though brand-new. It looked as if it had been destroyed during a crash landing, and had now been replaced. Next to the ship I could make out an almost primitive look-ing workshop which resembled a blacksmith's. Robots were bringing in bent and half-molten metal stays and braces, and when the automatons came out again they were carrying shiny new replacement parts to be used to strengthen the ship's hull.

I didn't need a commentary to know what had taken place.

The strangers, wherever they originally might have come from, had crash-landed on the planet with the two suns. Their spacecraft had been badly damaged during the attempt; they had repaired their ship and taken off again. It was quite clear: the dual-sun planet was not their home world.

At this moment the camera showed once more a total view of the partially repaired ship. The spaceship measured approximately 1,000 meters across, and its supporting legs were nearly 100 meters long.

Such a huge structure would hold tens of thou-sands of people!

Were these our gods? Our forefathers?

The next film-marble showed the takeoff, filmed from the ship.

I was then already familiar with satellite photos of our Earth, and *today* (I really mean "today," that is to say, in the year you are reading these words) I have been familiar for quite a while with the photos of our world taken from the moon. However, what I wit-nessed here was utterly fantastic.

The film showed the start and the journey of the starship through the universe, until it reached our cor-ner of the galaxy and our own planet Earth.

Readers of science fiction novels—and I not only read but also write them—understand about the pro-pulsion systems of interstellar vehicles. The main

problem is the speed of light, which must be exceeded
—yet Einstein's theories say that this is impossible to
achieve. The only "practical" solution would be hi-
bernation, placing the space travelers in a deep sleep
from which they wouldn't wake until they had arrived
at their destination.

But this dilemma was "solved" by science fiction
writers, who discovered an alternative.

They invented hyperspace.

They postulated that our normal universe is imbedded in another universe which is unknown to us.
An entirely different set of physical laws exists in this
other universe. Special space drives—and unbounded
energies—made it possible to break through from one
universe to the next. Once arrived in this hyperspace,
the spaceship could achieve any desired velocity.

This solved the problem of interstellar flights
without refuting Einstein.

The film I was watching now solved these difficulties in an entirely different manner: it simply ignored
Einstein's laws. The spaceship left the planet and its
two suns behind. The suns kept shrinking, soon to be
sparkling only like two distant stars amongst thousands
of other heavenly bodies, finally becoming lost completely.

And then the stars in the sky began to wander.
What an incredible, unimaginable sight!

I sat spellbound before my television screen, following the course of the speeding stars, my eyes wide
open with wonder. This was not a trick film. It was the
real thing! Absolutely genuine! The ship had surpassed
the speed of light and was racing through the cosmos
with unimaginable superspeed. And it was only with
the aid of a polarization process that it was possible
for the stars still to remain visible. Saenger's rainbow
did not appear.

The camera kept changing position and focus.
Now it aimed in the flight direction, then backward in
the opposite way. For the observer, the stars stood
close together in front of the craft's nose, then seemed
to diverge and fly past him. If one looked in the op-

posite direction, the stars squeezed back together to their original, densely packed state.

Then followed scenes from inside the ship.

The command center was—I simply find no other words to express my feelings—breathtaking: A gigantic hall, a semicircle, with dozens of instrument boards, videoscreens, switches, controls, scales, unknown devices—and with wide, upholstered swivel chairs in front for the technicians on duty.

There were also scenes showing life aboard the spaceship. I observed what went on in gyms, day-care centers, an indoor park with artificial sunlight, a swimming pool, school classes, higher-education centers, and a regular observatory. A great deal looked different from what I had imagined and written about in my novels, but the overall impression was quite similar.

Now it dawned on me what kind of a ship this was.

A spaceship carrying interstellar emigrants!

They were searching for a new home planet. Their old world might be overpopulated, and these people were willing to find a solution to this problem in this manner. They equipped a spaceship, took aboard volunteer passengers, and then started the long voyage into an uncertain future. Perhaps they had first sent out small scout ships to locate suitable planets and to chart the course?

Or had their home world been destroyed by a war? Had some catastrophe befallen their planet and rendered it uninhabitable? Did these strangers calculate that their only chance of survival lay in sending out ships to other worlds?

The film-marble ended as the starship's flight slowed down.

The stars stood still again.

I changed the film-marble. I had two more left. A glance at my watch told me it was almost 10 o'clock at night. I had set my watch by the sun's position after my visit with the commander. Time to prepare a cold meal from my provisions, and finally to allow myself the pleasure of a bit of whiskey. My hope that my hosts would send up some dinner to me had not materialized. They probably must be thinking that I would not feel like eating under these circumstances. They were wrong. I ate with a hearty appetite.

The fourth film-marble brought the final proof.

The camera kept pointing to the still-distant solar system, a sure sign that the course was already set. Earth was the destination of the alien astronauts. The sun grew larger; I estimated the spaceship was now traveling at half the speed of light.

Now I recognized the first planets: Saturn with its rings, Jupiter and its moon, and finally Mars.

And, at last—the Earth!

At the time when I set out on my journey into the past, we did not have yet the "photo of the century," that memorable picture taken in 1968 during the first manned orbital flight around the moon. It showed Earth from a distance of 386,000 kilometers: our own home planet as seen from its lonely satellite in the sky.

This film showed Earth from a point in space somewhere between Mars and Earth's orbit, about 30 million kilometers away. A blue-green planet; and nearby the moon, looking much smaller and almost white. The approach took place in precisely scheduled stages. I was no longer able to gauge the ship's velocity. Neither did I know the length of the intervals when the camera was not taking any picture. Not until Earth increased considerably in size, and the different filmed scenes became longer again, could I make calculations once more of how fast the craft was racing through space.

Its speed diminished markedly. I guessed the spaceship to be nearly 20,000 kilometers away from Earth when it entered into an orbital approach. The camera was filming now almost without interruption, although the images were projected in accelerated motion. Thus, one completed orbit around Earth lasted all of ten minutes—not much time to let all the details of Earth's surface properly sink into my mind.

Meanwhile, I had come to realize that this event must have occurred at least 20,000 years ago. There were many logical reasons for that. This provided an approximate clue to how far back into the past I had been transported by the time machine. And during the entire span of time, the continents had hardly changed as seen from this altitude. These shots could just as well have been taken from *Mercury, Gemini,* or *Vostok.* Only one tiny difference existed which became apparent only after a while: wherever the viewer's sight was not obscured by cloud banks that hid the Earth's surface, visibility was superior, and the outlines of land and water far easier to discern. In other words: Earth's atmosphere must have been cleaner and clearer than in my own present time. A logical conclusion, of course, since there existed no world-wide industrialization 20,000 years ago.

I was especially intrigued by one aerial view. The spaceship stood high above the Red Sea, not a single cloud impeding visibility. Up to one side, the contours of Europe were lying under a slightly cloudy sky but clearly recognizable. Africa and Europe displayed the same forms that I knew from our geographical maps. Not so, however, the east coasts of North and South America which were located—as seen from the spaceship—at the left edge of the globe and seemed strongly distorted along the North-South axis. Some areas were covered by haze and the viewer could only guess at what the coastline might be like.

Suddenly, I felt hot all over when I realized that I knew this view, knew it very well indeed. In my own present time existed a map, a map of the world, which had caused a great deal of excitement because it was irrefutably proven to be several centuries old—yet showed areas of Greenland and the Antarctic which were discovered at a much later date.

Did this mean that I had now participated in the actual birth of the legendary Piri-Reis maps?

The film continued. The ship was now descending on South America. The snow-covered Andes stood out clearly from the green and brown plains. The Amazon basin was gigantic, dark green with innumerable silvery river courses.

Either the film was now running through the projector with considerably increased speed, or the ship was now sinking toward the ground rather precipitously. After all, they were above an unknown planet and could not know what kind of dangers might await them. In my opinion, one ought to precede such a landing with weeks of observations made from space.

There was, of course, also the possibility that this observation period had been skipped on this film —I could not be sure of that. In any case, the aliens in their ship were falling toward the Andes with incredible speed.

I discovered Lake Titicaca.

It vanished from the upper edge of the screen, but came once more into view shortly before the actual touchdown. The ship landed in the vicinity of the southern lake shore, some 4,000 meters above sea level.

The journey had come to an end.

It was late, and I felt very tired. But the fifth and final film-marble might perhaps supply me with the ultimate explanation, and I was unable to fall asleep before then. During the last few hours I had been flooded with so many proofs for old beliefs and new insights that I felt my head swimming, but despite this I felt as happy as never before in my entire life. I now was certain that I was about to learn the whole truth, and at this moment I had no idea yet that all this was just the modest beginning.

Reality was still far more fantastic and incredible—and, as I was soon to find out, of a deadly logic.

The fifth film began after the landing had taken place. I could make out a lake shore about a kilometer away from the landing site. This had to be Lake Titicaca, although there seemed to be slight differences. The mountains appeared farther removed and the lake itself larger. From the air this fact had not been obvious to me, but it was quite noticeable now.

The settlers began to unload the ship's cargo.

Giant machines directed blinding-white beams of rays toward the nearby rocks, eating their way into the mountainside to create underground storage rooms. The settlers did not build temporary living quarters for themselves; they immediately went underground, inside the rock walls, as if they were already afraid of an impending attack.

It is impossible for me today to estimate the time that passed between the spaceship's landing and subsequent takeoff. But it was clear that the takeoff took place quite unexpectedly. The first images were blurred, indicating that someone had hurriedly picked up the camera and started filming without properly focusing. The camera lens followed the vertically-ascending spaceship, then again swung back to the people who obviously had been left behind against their will. Some settlers were waving, while others shook their fists in rage.

The ship rose faster until it disappeared in the clouds drifting above the lake.

The last scenes showed the settlers resuming their work after the ship's hasty departure.

The longer I thought about it, the less sense the whole incident seemed to make. If the aliens were really emigrants, then it was logical that the transport would take off again after having completed its mission. But why so precipitously? Perhaps even contrary to the wishes of the emigrants?

I turned the set off. The screen grew dark.

I lay stretched out on the bed—it was warm, and I needed no covers—wondering how to turn off the light. I did not like to sleep with the light on, for it reminded me unpleasantly of that time between 1939 and 1945, during the Second World War under the Nazi regime, when I was put in jail several times.

Where was the light switch? I looked around the room, but in vain.

Then, about ten minutes later, while I was resting on the bed, the light emanating from the walls and the ceiling became softer and softer, and gradually faded away completely.

Then it was dark.

Despite my fatigue, I could not fall asleep. Once more the entire film passed review before my closed eyes. It provided confirmation and enlightenment, but nevertheless, quite paradoxically, it brought up a thousand new questions. Questions for which I had to find an answer to bring back to Erich. He would not be satisfied with mere suppositions. He wanted the full truth, although I began to doubt he'd ever be able to publish it in a book.

I was still ignorant of what this truth actually consisted. And to what extent it would alter mankind's view of life—and the world as it developed during the past 2,000 years.

At some point—I don't know when—I fell asleep.

five

When I woke up I immediately glanced at my watch.

Ten o'clock!

I must have slept almost nine hours. I felt rested and refreshed. The light was burning again.

I heard a humming noise and realized that this sound had roused me from my sleep. The disagreeable feeling of being under constant surveillance intensified. I got up, washed, and dressed. Then I began to rummage rather dejectedly in my knapsack to find some food for my breakfast. Nobody seemed to feel hungry in this place! While I was still busy getting out my meager provisions, the door opened.

This time it was not the adjutant who came into my apartment. It was a young, pretty girl, carrying a heavily laden tray. Her black hair fell to her shoulders. The thin lips, delicate nose, and rounded cheeks reminded me again of the old Incas, although her features displayed a more alien character. This was what the women amongst the emigrants in the spaceship had looked like, exactly!

She wore sandals, a short Grecian skirt, a colorful, loosely-laced blouse, and a narrow golden circlet in her dark hair. She smiled as she noticed me busy with my knapsack, put the tray down on the table, and left the room. No word was spoken, but the smile had been enough.

The door closed silently.

I walked over to the table, my curiosity greatly aroused. What kind of food would they offer a visitor from their far distant future?

It was a bit of everything: Some mush, tasting faintly of bananas and curry. Also some very spicy cornbread—evidently baked together with hot peppers. Then a red, very sweet jelly, butter with a slightly sour taste—and cocoa.

After I had eaten my fill, the apartment began to get on my nerves.

I walked about the room a few times, then stopped in front of the door and contemplated the yellow button. If I pushed the button in, the door would open.

Should I or should I not?

Once again I was relieved from making this decision. I barely managed to step back when the door opened to reveal my adjutant. He gave me a friendly sign of greeting. He noticed at once that the position of the film-marbles had been changed, and nodded with satisfaction. I wasn't kept under surveillance, after all!

We communicated in signs. He inquired if my breakfast had been all right; I nodded my head. Then he pointed to the film-marbles; again I nodded. Asking him any questions would have been senseless. I had the feeling anyhow that I would find out everything very soon.

He made a few more gestures, trying to ascertain whether I had liked my bath and if I had slept well. He beckoned to me and pointed to the door. The invitation could not be misinterpreted: He wanted me to leave the room with him. I hesitated, then bent down and took the sphinx from my knapsack. Once again my adjutant nodded to express his approval. I remembered how strongly Erich had urged me never to lose sight of the little stone figure wherever I went.

In the corridor I discovered one of the ventilation ducts. It ended high up on the wall, very close to the ceiling. The long diameter of the sharp-rimmed, oval opening was about thirty centimeters and, as far as I could see, made of some material resembling pressed concrete.

We arrived at the elevator but did not stop to get on. Instead, we walked on till we reached the third side passage where we made a left turn. The adjutant came to a halt in front of the fourth door on the right side. I am able to give this exact description because I had to go the same way, unaccompanied, many times during the ensuing days.

The adjutant pressed the yellow button, encouraged me with a smile—and walked away, leaving me to my own devices.

I watched intently—waiting for the next surprise—as the door opened slowly. Beyond it was a brightly lit room, much larger than my own, filled with bookshelves and closed cabinets whose contents were hidden from view. In the background, close to the wall, was a wide, long table. A man was seated at the table, his back turned to me. He was writing.

He must have heard the door open but did not interrupt his work. Stacks of manuscripts and books lay on the table. I discovered a half-opened door to the right which permitted me a glimpse into an apartment similar to the one I called my own since yesterday.

Without turning around, the man spoke in a foreign language that seemed to have more vowels than consonants. It was the language of the astronauts who had landed in the big spaceship.

I entered the room and waited until the door closed behind me. Then I said: "Excuse me, but I can't understand you."

The man remained seated without moving for a few seconds, then jumped up. While he was still turning around, he stretched out his arms to greet me and called out: "Von X., is it *you* . . . ?" He stopped abruptly and studied me. He shook his head with a puzzled expression. "Who are you? Where do you come from?" Then his glance fell on the sphinx, which I clutched tightly in my hands.

I knew who this man was. It could be none other than Professor Thomé, who had traveled again back to the past and, to the rest of his own contemporaries, seemed to have vanished without a trace. "How did you get this statue?"

"Professor Thomé?" He nodded, bewildered, and sat down again. I pulled the chair up to the table and sat down. "I bring you greetings from Erich von X. He sent me here."

Thomé, still astonished, shook his head. "Pardon me if I seem so surprised, but I've been waiting for von X. for so many years. He didn't come. And now you are here instead, bringing with you the statue for identification. I believe you have some explaining to do, Mister . . . "

"Ernsting, Walter Ernsting."

"Well, Mr. Ernsting, you claim to have come on behalf of von X. I must ask you to supply me with some direct proof for this claim. Didn't he give you a letter for me? Why didn't he come personally?"

I placed the sphinx on the table. "He gave me this figure and asked me to undertake this journey in his place. He has neither time nor money for it, Professor. We are friends, and he trusts me. My work as a writer permits me to go frequently on trips. Von X. is busy writing a book. As soon as it is published, and if it becomes a success, he'll come in person. Till that time, however . . ."

Thomé regarded the sphinx and asked: "And how are things otherwise with our blond giant?"

"Erich has dark hair and isn't too tall," I replied calmly. "But go ahead, Professor, try to trip me up. You are entitled to that."

"You must understand," he said. "I must be

absolutely certain that Erich sent you. What can you tell me about Cairo in 1954?"

It was naturally quite easy for me to answer that request. Erich had described this incident at great length to me, and I still remembered vividly almost every word. When I mentioned the telepathic voice that kept calling me again and again, a satisfied smile played around the old professor's lips. I also made sure to repeat some of Thomé's own phrases he had used in his conversation with Erich, which my friend had conveyed almost word for word to me.

I fell silent.

"And how about you?" inquired the professor. "How did you get involved in this whole deal?"

"There seem to be close ties between Erich's existence and my own—if you don't believe that everything happens by chance. I have searched for him for thirty years, until I finally found him. On that occasion he asked me to travel to Cuzco on his behalf, to seek out Jacques Ferrant, and have him lead me to the pyramid. I complied with my friend's wishes. I opened the secret chamber, sat down in the time machine—and here I am."

Professor Thomé didn't seem to have aged too much, but in this respect Erich's description had been rather superficial and vague. Yet one thing was true, and had not changed: his eyes had remained young. I noticed this particularly now that he gazed at me piercingly. Then he nodded slowly. "I believe you, Walter. And please, forget about calling me 'Professor.' All right? How did they receive you here when you arrived?"

I gave him a brief account and concluded: "My apartment is not far from yours. Unfortunately, I don't understand a single word they are saying, but I watched five films last night . . . I don't know if you have seen them, too."

"I know them only too well. A copy would make Hollywood green with envy."

"Fine. Then I can save myself telling you about them, and can ask you some questions instead."

To my great surprise he shook his head. "Wait a while with your questions, Walter. First I want to explain these films to you. It's very easy to get the wrong impression if you aren't fully informed of the story behind them. I have lived here for many years with the aliens. I know their language. They keep no secrets from me, and they expected you—or rather Erich. We are their friends. But in the here and now, they have no friends, only enemies. They are ostracized, living in a foreign world that wants no part of them. They are waiting for an event. They know for certain it will come, but they don't know *when*—or whether any of them will survive the catastrophe." He waved me off as I tried to interject a remark. "Yes, I know what you want to say—the time machine! No, my friend, the time machine won't be of any help to them. They have my report and have found out through me that at least a few will escape their almost total annihilation. But there is no way to alter fate with the time machine. That which will happen *has long since taken place*. It is impossible to make it undone any more."

I've emphasized repeatedly my burning interest in the problem of the paradoxes of time travel, also that I have written a dozen novels dealing with this topic. Many of these works were mediocre, but with others I'd spend hours to write a single page in order to properly and logically construct the events caused by time shifts, time dilations, and so on. Sometimes I may have succeeded . . . and perhaps on other, frequent occasions, I failed.

This time, however, I was faced by a real situation! Fate confronted me with the problem which I knew only as a hypothetical assumption—and which I had to solve as best I could.

"It has already taken place?" I asked, totally perplexed and surprised. "What do you mean by that? Seen from this point in time, in which we now are, this catastrophe will take place only in the future. Why couldn't we prevent it from happening?"

Thomé folded his hands in his lap and thought a few seconds. He was searching for an analogy.

"Time is like a stream. Its source is the beginning, the most distant past, at the start of time. We are like a boat floating down this river, without a rudder, without an engine which could propel the boat either up- or downstream. The stream is flowing as through an eternity, but eventually it will flow into the ocean. I call that ocean, simply: The end of time. During this journey, let's assume, I find an oar, an engine. The time machine! It enables me to move again toward the source, upstream, back into the past. Do you follow me, so far?"

I nodded my head in assent. Of course, it was easy to understand. I had often enough used the same example to explain such phenomena in my own novels. I was most eager to know how he would use this allegory to explain the paradoxes of time.

He continued:

"While drifting downstream I passed a bend of the river where a tree trunk was lying in the eddy, obviously washed ashore and solidly anchored by underwater plants. Time flows past it, and the tree trunk has no influence on time or on whatever happens farther down the stream. I, on the other hand, can steer my motorboat into the little bay and push the tree trunk back into the mainstream. It will drift down, and perhaps someday it will ram another boat that is drifting without a rudder toward the future. Somebody may drown, and this person might be one of my forefathers. Thus an entire line ceases to exist, including myself. Therefore, I could not have pushed that tree trunk into the mainstream since I don't exist. But I *have done* it, and thus have extinguished my entire family line! The logical conclusion to be drawn from this deliberation is, therefore: I do exist as long as I remain in the past where I brought about that change. But as soon as I travel again into the future, the paradox takes effect. I will not arrive in my original future. I will cease to exist from the moment the catastrophe occurs, together with thousands of my ancestors. Do you follow me?"

Although this example wasn't quite clear to me, I

knew what he intended to express by it. I decided to return to this topic a bit later, as soon as I learned more of the aliens' story.

He pointed to a stack of manuscript, covered with writing. "This, Walter, is my report. You must bring it to von X. There is the entire story from the beginning but, believe me, it wasn't easy to reconstruct the events. A fragment here, a fragment there. It has taken years till I amassed that much, as you'll see here in my account. Nevertheless—I want you to know at once—many questions remain unanswered. Just to give you an example: There's nobody who knows who built the time machine. It was already here when the astronauts landed."

I stared at him, perplexed. "It was already here?"

He nodded. "Yes. As far as I am concerned, all facts point to the assumption that it was constructed in the far distant future; there are certain characteristics of the machine that would indicate it. Somewhere, sometime, there occurred a breakdown and the time-span determiner went out of commission. The machine will let you travel only for a fixed time span, not a day more, not a day less. About twenty-three thousand years." He left me time to recover from the shock and waited for my comment. I remained silent, for what could I have said? "This means if you stay here for two weeks and then return to your own present time, you'll find that two weeks have passed there, too. If, then, you remain two years in your own time and climb back again into the time machine to pay me another visit, I'll have to wait the same length of time until you arrive. Nobody has managed to correct that malfunction. That is the second reason why my friends, the aliens, cannot use the machine to save themselves. They have decided to lock the machine in a chamber and seal the entrance so that it will be discovered in twenty-three thousand years. Well, Walter, do you begin to see the connections?"

Very vaguely, I must confess. I looked at the manuscript. "When can I read it?"

He smiled. "Today you can take along the first part. It's almost completed. You'll stay long enough for me to finish it, won't you?"

I silently nodded my head, while a thousand questions flashed through my mind. Maybe, though, many would be answered in his report, so that I could save us both the trouble.

"We can visit each other at any time, as often as we want?"

"Why, of course," replied Thomé. "We are not prisoners here. And nobody will restrain you from leaving the building, but you mustn't be surprised if you find yourself with a constant companion. His sole purpose is to protect you. You might otherwise get lost on the grounds. Or a robot might mistake you for an enemy. They've been programmed as guards."

We chatted for a while longer, then I returned to my apartment, carrying with me the first part of Thomé's report. Some time later, the girl brought my meal, with a bottle of wine and some fruit. Since I did not feel like leaving my apartment again, and particularly since my curiosity would not let me rest, I flung myself on my bed and began to read. Thomé's handwriting was as fine as print. It was small and dainty but easy to read.

Professor Marcel Thomé's Report

About 40,000 years before Christ's birth, an explorer ship of the Altairians landed for the first time on Terra, our Earth. The explorers had been charged with this mission by the Galactic Colonization Council in order to catalog systems with inhabitable planets. Since the astronauts had encountered on Earth half-intelligent races, this planet was no longer suitable to be settled by the Altairian people; it proved, however, to be of interest to the Council of Biological Surveillance. The Galactic Medical Council issued a permit to establish a base on Earth. Shortly afterward the experiments were started.

Modern-day science has never come up with a satisfactory explanation for the sudden appearance of an advanced human race that followed and replaced primitive Neanderthal man. It seemed logical that naturally-caused mutation had caused this phenomenon which produced Cro-Magnon man, our direct ancestor.

The truth is that 40,000 years ago the Altairians captured diverse hominid groups in South Africa, in the Sahara, in northern Europe, and in Mongolia. Then the aliens subjected their captives to a process of transforming their genes. By changing the sequence of bases in the DNS-macromolecule, the Altairian scientists cultivated artificial genes in their laboratories. After the growth of the programmed chain of chromosomes was completed, they were used for artificial insemination by introducing this "sperm" directly into the uterus of female hominids. The males of the primitive species were rendered sterile by exposing them to properly adjusted doses of radiation. They could continue to indulge in their sexual drive and believe the newborn offspring to be their own. This had the advantage that the male hominids would protect their mates as well as their young from all dangers of the environment. Eventually these newborn—and also mutated—young ones became fertile again!

Similar experiments were conducted by the Altairians all over the galaxy. Their purpose was to further the general development of civilizations that remained independent, so that they could become members of the already existing Galactic Federation that much faster. This procedure proved to be a timesaver; nothing was left to chance.

The colonizing council concerned itself in principle only with those worlds where intelligent life forms had not yet evolved. It gathered the reports of the recognizance fleet and distributed the mandates to settle these particular planets.

It was not easy to obtain a permit to settle on a free planet, because there were not enough inhabitable free worlds. On most planets which circled within the ecosphere around their sun, there existed at least the beginnings of intelligent life. This was the reason illegal dealings with voluntary but not registered emigrants became a great business for shady characters.

These people had their connections find out where and when a new world was catalogued. Nobody knew what methods they employed. And any emigrant who eventually became wise to their questionable business dealings could not do too much about it. By that time it was already too late for the poor victims.

As regards Earth, the experiments were discontinued after four decades as soon as the results proved positive. The new breed of the Cro-Magnon man was already far more intelligent as a child than any adult Neanderthal man. The Galactic Medical Council called back its representatives, for they were needed on other worlds.

The only trace of the Altairian research expedition that stayed behind on Earth was a small control base. It was completely automated, radioing its report to the control council at regular intervals. The control base also checked on the activity of warning probes which orbited around the planet as artificial satellites. The probes' special mission was to warn any spaceship belonging to the Galactic Federation away from landing on Earth. Any intervention—however insignificant it might be—into the further development of the successfully mutated new species of man was strictly forbidden.

Nearly 20,000 years went by.

Mankind continued in its upward-bound development—free from any outside interferences. Man became more and more intelligent, and kept progressing—but never managed to detect the secret base of the extraterrestrials, which might still exist on Earth right up into the twentieth century.

During the Ice Age, hunters migrated from Asia across the frozen Bering Straits into North America and settled the empty land, so far devoid of any human life. Slowly they advanced south. When they reached the land bridge between the Northern and Southern Hemispheres, a completely unanticipated event took place.

An illegal emigrant spaceship of the Altairians landed on Earth.

The ship's commander had collected huge sums of money from the unsuspecting passengers. With the help of special transmitters, he had skillfully neutralized the warning probes of the control station so that it could not register the arrival of unauthorized settlers. Before the emigrants realized that they had been put down on an already-inhabited world, which thus was a forbidden zone for any galactic colonists, the criminal commander had already fled with his ship and his illegal gains. The commander made certain that no hyperspace radio transmitter capable of bridging the vast intergalactic distances remained on Earth, and the next direct check on the control station would not take place for another 300 years.

The unfortunate settlers realized they had to make good use of this period of grace. They knew what fate to expect as illegal emigrants. They would be exterminated as soon as their presence on the taboo planet should be detected. On the other hand, they also knew that they had 300 years in which to erase their traces on this world. Nothing must remain to arouse the Galactic Control Council's suspicions. Their own survival and that of their descendants would depend on their successful concealment.

This also clears up the question of why we hardly ever find any clues that we had visitors from outer space some 23,000 years ago. The Altairian emigrants themselves tried their best to hide any traces of their presence here on Earth. In addition to that, they did something else to be absolutely safe.

Although they had a few machines at their disposal, as well as some robots and other instruments, they had to go one step further, in order to vanish without a trace: use camouflaging techniques and mix with the already-existing population.

There was, fortunately, no problem of having different chromosomes for, as expected, the offspring of the mutated hominids of 40,000 years earlier had won out over their tribal brethren of that period. And *these* —the descendants alive in our day and age—have twenty-three chromosomes. This is the characteristic number for all "hominids" of the Galactic Federation!

South America was not yet settled by human beings, but the high altitude of the Andes offered the most favorable living conditions for the stranded Altairians. They sent out special troops in gravity gliders to hunt small groups of the Mongol-type Ice Age hunters in North America. The commando troops brought these people—crazed out of their senses with superstitious fear—into the highlands of the Andes and settled them there. This way the Altairian emigrants transferred a part of the so-called Folsom culture of North America to another continent.

Wanting to achieve an even greater degree of perfection in this camouflage maneuver, other commandos captured descendants of Cro-Magnon man who had migrated throughout the millennia to the eastern and southern parts of Asia, and flew them into the icy wastelands of northern Alaska. There they were supposed either to become acclimatized to the cold environment or else to migrate to the warmer south. This southward trek never took place, however. The displaced tribes adjusted to the cold climate and settled permanently in the polar region. Today their descendants are known to us as Eskimos.

Meanwhile work was begun near the landing place today called Tiahuanacu. Giant bunkers were built in the rocks to provide protection against nuclear attack. Some native Earthmen were employed in this construction work. The primitive Earthlings grew gradually used to the fact that they had been transported into the land of the gods.

The fourth generation of the Altairians left the original colony at Lake Titicaca and traveled north and northwest. They settled in the mountains of Cuzco and started to build a structure for survival, which I knew later on as the glass labyrinth. [Professor Thomé

is referring here to the crystal labyrinth.—Clark Darlton]
Other members of the original settlement explored the
other continents with the remaining gliders—always
careful not to give away their presence to the control
base. Some liked the warmer climates, adjusted to the
denser atmosphere of the lowlands, took wives, and
founded new settlements.

The date of the inspection was drawing close, but
300 years and almost four generations had sufficed to
obscure the memory of their origin. Only two gravity
gliders were left. The others had broken down and
could not be repaired. Also, most of the robots had
used up their energy reserves. Having become useless,
they wandered into the blast furnaces to be melted
down as scrap metal.

The settlers discovered the time machine, but were
not in a position to do anything with it. Not until I,
Professor Thomé, found the time machine in the year
1934 A.D. and traveled back in time for the first time,
did the Altairians learn what kind of a discovery they
had made.

It was impossible for them to utilize this knowledge for their own benefit. They could not escape their
fate, and only my assurance that some of the group
would be saved from destruction prevented them from
sinking into total despair. Everyone believes, of course,
he'll be one of the lucky survivors. The construction
of the glass labyrinth is being continued, and the time
machine will be sealed inside the secret chamber.

I have seen the films taken by the Altairian emigrants, but there is nothing in them to enlighten us
about the forbidden enterprise. They were forced to
make an intermediate landing on a by-now unknown
planet with two suns, when the commander noticed
some damage in the spaceship's power drive. The stopover lasted almost one year.

The expected inspection did not take the settlers
by surprise. But despite all precautions, the current
commander of the Altairian settlers fears that the control mission must have grown suspicious—a fact I can
unfortunately confirm. The annihilation of the emi-

grants is impending, but it is impossible to determine exactly at what time. I have tried to calculate it.

The starships of the Altairians and their superiors, the Galactic Federation, fly with the speed of light. When I saw the film for the first time, however, I had the impression that they could exceed the speed of light. And this is indeed the case, as I have been assured. The effect of the wandering stars occurs because of the dilation of time. The journey from Altair to Earth actually lasts not more than three years, while sixteen years are passing on Earth.

The inspection occurred about four years after my first visit, in my own present time: that would be about 1938. When I returned to the Altairians in 1964, the same stretch of time, namely twenty-six years, had meanwhile passed. That meant that the mission of annihilation would be carried out in about six years —provided the authorities had given their permission without any delay. The same interval of six years would, of course, also elapse in our modern time era. No change in a difference of time is possible; both time planes are running parallel.

At the earliest, then, it would happen in six years, maybe a bit later.

I wondered and worried if on that occasion the time machine would be endangered or even destroyed. There are only six more years left, no more. Therefore any attempt to visit the past once again might be fraught with deadly danger.

The continuation of my report deals with the future as seen by the Altairians. I'll try to reconstruct the further events from the present state of my knowledge, and that which we shall have learned in the far-ahead future days of 1965.

* * *

I rearranged the papers in a neat stack and placed them on the table. I had become so enthralled by this short report that I had lost track of the time. I looked at my watch.

Evening had come.

I could not quite understand Thomé's statement about the potential destruction of the time machine. Or had Thomé expressed himself in a vague fashion? What did he mean by saying that the machine would only exist for another six years? Seen from the year 1965, this time machine would have already been destroyed 23,000 years ago. If it was annihilated in the past, then it could not exist in 1965!

The girl returned with food. I tried to start a conversation with her, but she merely smiled and left.

Have it your way, I thought to myself. I devoted my attention to an excellent platter of cold cuts.

After I finished eating, I decided to pay a visit to the professor with my questions.

I entered his apartment as he was replacing a book in his bookcase. He pointed to a chair. "Have a seat, Walter. By tomorrow the first part of my report will be completed. You can give it to Erich, but I must ask him not to publish a word of it. The world isn't ready for it yet. Nobody will believe the truth."

I sat down. "Truth is too fantastic," I agreed with him.

"Correct!" He nodded his approval. "You have read my report?"

"Yes. I can't quite understand all of it. One thing seems clear though. We cannot change the fate of the Altairians."

"Unfortunately. You are right. If they tried to flee into the future it would unleash a chain of catastrophes. The Incas, mainly descendants of the emigrated Mongols and Ice Age hunters, interbred with the Altairians, would simply disappear. Columbus would find goodness knows what, but no highly developed culture. No gold for Spain, no continued exploring of the New World. America would remain practically untouched. Besides, what do you think would happen if ten thousand Altairians suddenly appeared in the twentieth century and asked for asylum?" Thomé shook his head. "No, that would be impossible!"

"And the Altairians, how do they feel?"

"They realize that any attempt to flee with the

time machine would foil the hundred-thousand-year plan of the Galactic Federation—and that they would face a far worse punishment than what they are expecting now. No, there is no time machine for them. There is no possibility of escape. They are fully aware of this, but they also know that maybe one hundred of their people will survive the catastrophe. Everyone, of course, fondly hopes to be one of the lucky ones. That is why they are so calm. And that is our good fortune, too!"

Things were beginning to be clear to me. "The Galactic Federation, Thomé—do you believe it still exists today? Do you believe it's still keeping our Earth under surveillance?"

"Yes! The controllers in charge of surveillance know they failed at the time to annihilate all the illegal emigrants from Altair. They have witnessed how the survivors—unintentionally—founded the religions of the world. How they became the instigators of all that is at the base of our cultural life, and thus messed up everything that had originally been planned in the Galactic Federation's great master plan. But who can be held accountable for this unwanted development at this date, after twenty-three thousand years!"

Now I understood why the Altairians preferred the uncertainty of survival in the past to the flight into the deadly certainty of the future. They chose to remain so that one per cent of their group might survive!

And this one per cent later on would determine the path in which development of life here on Earth would run!

"Will you discuss that in your final report?"

"Yes, I will. How long do you intend to stay here?"

"Just a few days. Can I leave any time I want to? Will they try to hold me back?"

"No. They will hardly pay attention to you. Make good use of this time, Walter. Have a look around the past. We have a glider that will take you anywhere you desire. I need another three to four weeks to finish my report."

"Four weeks?" I began to worry. True, my publisher had agreed to give me a vacation, but four weeks was a long time. "That long?"

"I won't need all this time to write down my account, but there are a few trips I still want to take, to check facts."

* * *

Two weeks went by.

I usually left my apartment after lunch to take a look around the plateau. I was especially interested in watching the progress in the construction of the crystal labyrinth. It seemed to be near completion. Huge blocks of rock brought out from inside the mountain were piling up high at the foot of the hill. This is where they would be lying for more than 21,000 years, until the Incas were ready to establish their rule and build their temples of the sun. These regularly shaped stones would be a present of the gods for the Inca architects. They simply took them and erected the fortress of Sacsayhuaman.

Being exposed to the weather while lying in the open for twenty-one millennia caused the glaze of the rock chunks to disappear. Though they were still smooth, almost as though cut and polished, they lacked any visible clue to their origin. It was different, though, in the interior walls of the labyrinth. Wind, rain, and snow had hardly affected them. No sensible person would assume that the Incas had vibration milling-cutters or laser saws at their disposal, but the obvious assumption that the labyrinth might have been built from the waste products of an earlier structure by extraterrestrial intelligences seemed just too fantastic.

And now I was standing here on the plateau watching how robots and gravity transporters were carefully towing and steering the laser-cut blocks to the foot of the hill.

The adjutant issued a few instructions to a work detachment, then came toward me, a friendly smile on his face. In the past few days, we had managed to work out an effective sign language to communicate with each other. For simplicity's sake, I'll attempt to render our silent talks in the form of dialogues.

"Well, how do you like it?" he asked, and pointed to the entrance of the labyrinth.

"Your work is progressing, Adjutant. The result will outlast our entire history, many thousands of years."

He led me off to one side to a small, closed-off cave that had only one wide entrance. Inside the cave was a glider, a flat "boat" with an open cabin and without wings.

"Will you accompany me on one of my inspection flights?"

I nodded to indicate I was pleased to accept this invitation, for I had been waiting for just such an opportunity.

The seats in the glider were arranged behind each other. The adjutant sat before me. The open cockpit bothered me, not just because of the cold. Fortunately, I had put on a pullover and a windbreaker. I knew that the gliders were independent of the thin atmosphere's lifting capacity and its speed. These machines were capable of hovering motionless in the air just like a balloon, so there was no danger of encountering a strong head wind. Besides, the sun was shining out of a clear blue sky, and it was almost noon.

The glider lifted off slowly, rose to a height of a few meters, then glided toward the edge of the plateau. We were protected from the wind by a windshield in front of the adjutant's seat. I enjoyed an unimpeded view to both right and left.

Over to the side where later on Cuzco, the capital city of the Incas, would rise, nothing was to be seen. And the mountain Sacsayhuaman, which later was to be known as the famous hill of the falcons, was now merely rock-strewn soil and patches of grass. I found no trace of human settlements except for a few small houses nestled deep down in a small valley. The adjutant explained that these were the abodes for a few of the laborers' families.

These primitive stone huts gave no inkling of the future splendor of the Inca buildings. Yet these people down there were the direct forefathers of that proud nation. The inhabitants of the tiny settlement, mainly women, children, and old men, were not frightened by the sight of the glider overhead. For them it was not an unusual spectacle to see the vehicle of the gods appear in the sky. Only the priest—he already wore a wooden headdress—prostrated himself on the ground, then raised his arms in an imploring gesture toward heaven.

The adjutant set course toward the southeast and skillfully curved his way along the fertile Urubamba Valley. The glider's speed increased but the temperature remained bearable.

I gradually became used to this novel sensation of flight. We were floating without the slightest sound or vibration through the air, just like a balloon. I felt weightless, as if detached from Earth, though naturally I was still subject to Earth's gravitational pull. There was not a trace of discomfort, not even when the adjutant came in close above steep, rocky crags or deep, lateral valleys.

We had been flying about two hours when we sighted Lake Titicaca below us. We had therefore covered a distance of some 280 kilometers. I had a good idea what our destination would be.

Tiahuanacu!

In 23,000 years this area would be the site of a mysterious field of ruins. Now I perceived no ruins, but a palace similar to the one in Cuzco. Work was going on in the nearby rocky mountainside. Were they building another installation here for survival?

We touched down on the plain between the palace and the mountains. The natives and the Altairians gave a friendly but respectful welcome to my adjutant. They greeted me with such cordiality that I almost felt embarrassed. I knew that this reception was really intended for another man who should have been standing here instead of me.

The adjutant showed me around, obviously proud of their handiwork. It was impossible to ignore the resemblance to the installations at Cuzco. Thousands of years later, in my own present time, there would be considerable differences between the two sites, due to the more protected location of Cuzco, and to the Incas, who utilized the debris from the Altairian construction site to erect temples.

The sun was descending in the west when we started out again. This time we flew faster and straighter. I ducked down in my seat to escape the biting cold. The adjutant did not seem to be bothered by the freezing temperature. On his home planet in the Altair system, sixteen light-years from Earth, such temperatures apparently were the norm.

Two hours later we landed in Cuzco.

I thanked the adjutant and ambled over to my apartment, overwhelmed by the flood of new impressions, and physically exhausted.

But when I entered my room all my tiredness vanished.

Next to the tray with my supper I saw the rest of Thomé's manuscript.

His report was complete.

I repressed my curiosity long enough to appease my hunger. Then I stretched out on the bed and began to read.

Professor Thomé's report was not very long.

Second Report of Professor Thomé

Assuming the time machine is set for exactly 23,000 years, and provided this adjustment cannot possibly be changed, I therefore am living now in the year 21,035 B.C.

This means that the annihilation of the descendants of the illegal emigrants from Altair is to take place around the year 21,029. Carried over into my own era, the two critical dates would be 1965 and 1972.

Until that time, the time machine can be used without any risk.

What will happen to it after that date nobody knows yet.

The historical events of modern times are well

known. The Incas themselves handed little to us directly; modern historians depend more on deduction than on actual facts. The first emigrants came from Asia, Ice Age hunters who founded the Folsom culture in North America. According to official data, these primitive hordes swept to the south and reached the Andes about 11,000 B.C.

Of course, I realize now that this migration occurred some 10,000 years earlier, and that it was brought about by the Altairians and their antigrav gliders.

When the long-awaited and much feared punitive action of the Galactic Federation was carried out, a huge catastrophe befell our planet. The memory of this horrible event survived over the span of many thousands of years. Later on, these happenings were interpreted by geologists and archaeologists according to their own preconceived way of thinking.

The installations near Tiahuanacu were (or are being) destroyed, and I don't know if there were any survivors there. The executioner's fleet of the Galactic Federation must possess accurate detection and tracking instruments which enabled them to ferret out the descendants of the Altairians.

It is difficult to take a moral stand on this punitive action. I, personally, absolutely reject such radical measures, but on the other hand I must admit that the mere existence and subsequent activities of the emigrants have decisively influenced the cultural life of the human race on Earth. Maybe everything would have turned out entirely different and better without them. Maybe the seeds of war, distrust, hatred, and racial discrimination would not have arisen in homo sapiens if it had not been for extraterrestrial interbreeding.

The fleet of the Galactic Federation carried out its mission of destruction on all continents. Everywhere that Altairian colonies could be found, there came a rain of fire and glowing stones from the skies—according to the eye-witness reports of long since died-out peoples. It must be assumed that nuclear weapons and laser rays were deployed in these missions.

The crystal labyrinth must have been subjected to a regular fire storm, for chambers and hallways are telescoped into each other, and entrances as well as walls are glazed by molten rock. Anyone who wishes can check out these facts. Just turn your back to the Inca fortress Sacsayhuaman, and you will stand before glazed rocks and debris and remains from the labyrinth that rolled down from the mountains onto the plateau of the Falcon Rock. Very few Altairians could have survived this catastrophe.

This was the first day the gods died.

After the fleet left, the survivors dug out from their underground shelter. They knew that the mission had left behind on Earth a control base manned by regular members of the surveillance council, and later events proved the truth of this assumption.

This meant that the punitive action might be resumed as soon as they found out about the existence of survivors. Luckily for the few who had escaped the holocaust, the base did not have at its disposal the same horrible weapons of destruction as the original group.

The surviving Altairians faded from view by mingling and intermarrying with the native population.

During the course of the ensuing millennia, it became increasingly difficult for the Galactic Federation to intervene, because of their laws that forbade any interference in the internal affairs of the natives. The remaining Altairians had become almost like natives themselves. Only their memories, that grew ever more vague and indistinct, linked them to their past. But even that last memory began to fade, and turned into legend and myth.

As an example of such a memory surviving to modern times, I'd like to mention here Manco Capac, a direct descendant of the "sons from the heavens," who is supposed to have founded the line of the Incas. According to legend, he emerged together with three brothers and four sisters from a cave thirty kilometers southeast of Cuzco. Their other companions emerged from caves situated farther away, and then joined Capac and his siblings as their followers. Capac and his brothers and sisters were known as the "sons of the sun god." No doubt, this Capac was a descendant of the Altairians.

I wonder if he realized it.

Also, on the other continents, the memory of the past became submerged in the ocean of time. One or two gliders must have been around for quite a while still; the legends of the nations all over the world tell of them. Then they, too, vanished. Perhaps they crashed into the ocean or were hidden away in a safe place. Also the remaining energy weapons play a considerable role in various traditions and religious writings. Nordic gods hurled lightning strokes and thunderbolts; on Mount Sinai the 10 Commandments were burned into the rock by laser rays; and if anywhere in the world a demigod split rocks with his bare fist, he most certainly accomplished this feat with the help of a laser pistol.

In short, time contributed its own share to obliterate all traces of reality. What remained was legend . . . fading memories . . . and the belief that the vanished gods would return some day.

Peru owes the landing strips of Nazca to this very same belief. I do not believe that they were installed by the Altairians; they tried their best to avoid drawing attention to their presence on Earth. Such artificially planned runways, such exact patterns, would have been impossible to overlook by anyone approaching Earth from space. Therefore, these lines were not constructed by the Altairians but rather by those people in whom the memory of the "gods" was still alive. These gigantic drawings are older than assumed by modern-day geologists and archaeologists. Neither can we rely in this case on the Carbon-14 method. If someone applied this method to determine the age of a piece of charcoal found on such a runway, he would succeed in obtaining the age of that particular piece of charcoal—but definitely not the age of the rocky ground on which it was found.

One thing is certain: The control base of the Galactic Federation is still in operation today, in the twentieth century A.D.

It keeps watching over mankind's development. It might be camouflaged as a religious institution or a political authority in Europe, Asia, America, or even in Africa. But it exists.

After viewing some films depicting many examples of the high level to which Altairian technology had risen, I am inclined to believe that this surveillance station is functioning somewhere on Earth as an independent secret base. I believe it has been programmed so that at some point in time it will reveal itself, at least to some chosen individual.

That moment might reunite mankind with the Galactic Federation, and lead us back again to the stars.

But the road back into space, from where at least one line of our ancestors came, will never be open for us as long as we are practicing intolerance on our home planet. Only those who show respect toward any life form, even if different from us in appearance, way of thinking, and feeling, can be judged worthy to start out on their homeward trek to the stars, to become an active participant in the intergalactic family.

Between the years 7000 B.C. and 3000 B.C. there was undoubtedly a very important and influential control base in the high valley between Lebanon and Anti-Lebanon, in the area of modern Baalbek. Innumerable proofs exist for this even today: the dancing ground of the giants, for which we can offer no explanation unless we accept the fact that this was the place where formerly the supply ships and surveillance craft of the colonial authorities used to land. Within a radius of about 2,000 kilometers, all cutural "explosions" occurred. Jericho came into being—the oldest city of the world and a model settlement. Sodom and Gomorrah were destroyed by a nuclear bomb—for reasons unknown to us. Just think of the Sumerians, whose origin is not known: Akkad, Babylon, Nineveh, or the legend of Prometheus in the Caucasus, who brought the gift of fire to man. Which fire? Ordinary fire was already well known at that time. Lebanon itself was regarded as "forbidden territory," and a certain Gilgamesh was the first to penetrate into that land. He encountered a robot (whom he defeated), witnessed a nuclear explosion, and saw a spaceship. He described an energy screen and hypnobarriers—all this information can be read in modern translations.

There cannot be any doubt that one of these control bases we are looking for existed at that time in Lebanon, and it influenced the entire cultural development of the then known world.

Belief—what actually is belief? Nothing but the most primitive way ever devised by the growing awareness of awakening life-forms of facing the undeniable fact that death is inevitable. This gave rise to our religions, which had to exist of necessity. But the appearance of the presumed gods anthropomorphized the forces of nature that man had worshipped thus far. They were given names which they have retained to this day.

And now a final word of warning for those who have become doubters of the established truths as a result of their research and deliberations.

It is dangerous to search for the truth. And it may be fatal to find it.

I have found it. Therefore I no longer desire to return to my own age. I'll stay here with my friends, the Altairians. Together, we will face the impending catastrophe, and either survive or die. One thing is certain: The day the attack is launched against us from the cosmos, I shall also learn the final truth.

It is a truth I shall keep for myself alone, and I shan't be able to communicate it to any other person. Not even to my friend Erich von X., who is on its track.

I hope and pray that he'll never find it.

For it is the most important and most deadly truth in the world.

* * *

I gathered up the neatly written pages and placed them together with the first part of Professor Thomé's manuscript. I closed my eyes.

The report was but a few pages long, but it deposed man from the throne he had built for himself. This account changed the world, all moral laws, any ethical foundation—and our alleged treasure of accumulated knowledge.

However, more far-reaching and fraught with danger than that: Its publication would alert the control base of the extraterrestrials. It was self-evident that Erich von X.'s life was imperiled from the first moment his book would be published, unless he was smart enough to rest content with mere allusions and question-posing. He ought to restrict himself to stimulating his contemporaries to reexamining their way of thinking. Then the extraterrestrial control station, which then might leave him alone. For the belief in gods, whatever their names, was an unplanned outcome of the illegal emigrants' actions, and it had decisively hampered mankind's development.

One thing was crystal clear to me:

Erich must learn the truth . . . but he must never publish it in a book.

Knowledge of the truth should serve him only as a moral elevation and a new impetus to pursue further this new-found revelation.

Mulling over these thoughts and the decision I had arrived at, I finally fell asleep.

* * *

I remained till the beginning of December—at least it was December according to my little pocket calendar I had brought with me. Which month it actually was in the year 21,035 B.C., I didn't know. Professor Thomé wasn't able either to enlighten me on that point; he guessed it to be March or April. And when all was said and done it didn't really matter.

The Altairians were still busy constructing the labyrinth, but lately some difficulties had arisen with some of the half-tamed natives. They had recently arrived with a transport from the southern regions of the North American continent, and after an initial period of adjustment had agreed to work for the "sons of the gods." All of a sudden, however, they had failed to show up for work.

This was not a catastrophe; the loss was easily made up by robots. But that was beside the point. What really mattered for the Altairians was the greatest possible involvement of humans in this construction work. This would facilitate the erasure of their tracks.

The second cause for alarm lay in the unforeseen activities of the escaped savages who tried to incite other barbarians against the Altairians, leading them to believe they could find quick and easy loot.

Soon after the marauders had staged their first raids on the settlements of the loyal workers, the commander proceeded to take the necessary countermeasures.

Guerrilla warfare broke out, both sides fighting with the same kind of weapons. The Altairians could deploy their far superior ray-guns only in case of extreme emergency, for fear of detection by the control base, whose instruments were capable of registering large spurts of energy across the face of half the globe —provided these energy bursts were not shielded by rock walls.

Using the same weapons as the savages, the Altairians proved no match for their primitive foes. Reports came in with increasing frequency that some patrol of the "sons from heaven" had been ambushed and killed.

A short while before I climbed again into the time machine to return to my own era, I revisited the hill where many years later the fortress of Sacsayhuaman was to be constructed. I was eager to have everything firmly fixed in my memory so that I could give a detailed report to Erich, and said so to Thomé.

"Sounds very reasonable, my friend," he said. "The adjutant will be pleased to fly you over. Don't forget to take your sphinx along."

"The sphinx?" I was honestly astonished. I hadn't touched the stone figure for many weeks, since I never needed it. "Why?"

"You already know, Walter, that the group at

Tiahuanacu is building some installations similar to the ones we have here near Cuzco. They have finished there some secret chambers which can be opened only with the help of a special key: the sphinx. I'd like to have a look at these chambers."

"You mean to say that you will accompany me to Tiahuanacu?"

"Yes, Walter, we'll start out tomorrow!"

The next day we flew to Lake Titicaca.

We found there, of course, the same trouble with the natives as in Cuzco. When Professor Thomé explained to the adjutant that we planned an excursion into the nearby mountains, he warned us and suggested we should take some companions along for our protection. We declined with thanks. I carried my knapsack on my back with a few provisions—and, of course, my sphinx.

But we neglected to take along any weapons.

* * *

It was morning when we set out, and we kept up a steady pace to reach the nearby hills. I did not know where Thomé had learned how to get to our goal, but it looked as if he was very sure of our destination.

"What do you expect to find in these secret chambers?" I inquired.

"Definitely not a second time machine. Certainly some interesting items. I want to see the chambers, nothing else."

Our way led us past one of the many construction sites. It struck me that only robots, machines, and some Altairians were at work there. There was not a single native in sight.

Our path grew steeper and steeper. It led through bizarre rock formations, and it was plain to see that it was formerly very heavily traveled by pedestrians. Sparse new vegetation had begun to make its appearance in some places; the path clearly had not been in regular use for quite some time.

At the entrance to a cave in the rock wall, Thomé halted.

"They have laid out these chambers so that the opening mechanism cannot be affected by any outside climatic conditions. I assume they were built to serve as future emergency storage depots, and that they contain all kinds of materials to make life easier for any survivors after the catastrophe."

We looked around to make sure that we had not been followed. Then we entered.

The cave soon narrowed to a corridor; then, some twenty meters through the solid rock, it widened again to form a large room with no detectable exit.

I took my lamp and carefully searched the wall. Thomé helped me, examining the smooth rock with probing fingertips. We probably would never have found the separating wall had we not quite accidentally stumbled over the "keyhole."

It was located in the rock wall close to the ground, hardly ten centimeters above it. The work seemed to have been done rather carelessly; there were several such recesses in the wall which were most likely intended to mislead the uninitiated. We, however, noticed immediately the typical shape of the hole—almost rectangular except for the two indentations below for the legs and another notch above for the tail of the stone figure.

"Here it is!" Thomé exclaimed. As I took the sphinx out of my knapsack, he snatched it out of my hands and tried to insert it in the hole.

Suddenly we became aware of a noise.

At first I thought it came from the opening mechanism as it was being set in motion. But the figure was only halfway inserted into the "keyhole." Thomé had not found quite the right knack for turning the "key." Finally, it seemed to work.

Again that noise; this time much closer.

I tapped the professor lightly on the shoulder and extinguished the light.

"What's the matter?" he wanted to know.

"Shh! Somebody's coming!" I whispered into his ear.

He slowly straightened up from his kneeling position. "We'd better leave the sphinx here," he said softly. "You can pick it up later. The Altairians must never find out that we intended to abuse their confidence."

But these were not Altairians who had pursued our tracks—as we were soon to find out.

Putting on an innocent air, and again holding the brightly shining lamp in my hand, we approached the cave exit.

When we realized our mistake!

Howling like a pack of wolves, a horde of savages attacked us. Due to the unusual way we were dressed, they probably believed us to be some especially high-ranking sons of the heavens. Any attempt to defend ourselves was senseless, so we resigned ourselves to our fate without offering any resistance. Perhaps that was why they did not kill us on the spot. They tied our hands with primitive grass ropes and drove us high into the mountains to their hideouts.

We spent the night in a small cave which was protected from wind and rain by an overhanging rock shelf. We were as cold as a brass monkey because our wild captors did not light a fire. Maybe they had not yet learned this art!

Thomé was extremely depressed. For a long time he did not utter a sound, then he apologized: "I'm sorry to have placed you in such a terrible situation. I should have curbed my curiosity."

"Don't blame yourself for this. Besides—we are still alive." I did not feel angry at him, but I was naturally greatly concerned. "What do you suppose they are planning to do with us, Thomé?"

I could feel that he shrugged his shoulders. We were lying close together on the ground, our hands and legs firmly bound with grass ropes.

"I wouldn't be a bit surprised if they'd consider us as a welcome addition to their meager menu. They are cannibals. They believe they acquire both the strength and intelligence of their foes when they eat them."

I shuddered, admiring the professor's sangfroid. He had nerve! Occupying his mind with socioeconomic observations while those savages outside were already sharpening their knives . . .

I slept very fitfully during that helpless, despairing night. The adjutant could not possibly leave us in the lurch! Surely tomorrow morning he would make a systematic aerial search for us. If we could only manage to give some sign, there was a real chance of being saved. Flying machines still instilled respect in the wildest savages . . . I hoped.

When day broke we were still alive. They untied our legs—probably because they did not feel like carrying their dinner! Beating us with their fists, they chased us farther up the now very narrow path, toward the peak of the mountain. They had given us nothing to eat, but neither Thomé nor I felt the slightest hunger. I had long since managed to lose my knapsack with its small supply of food and, as I suddenly realized, the checkbook I had stowed in one of the side pockets.

But what good would money do me at the moment?

The horde stopped on a plateau just below the top of the mountain. Other tribesmen trotted out from caves in the rocks, yelling and howling, to celebrate the capture of the much feared sons of the heavens. Thomé and I were treated liberally to some blows, which were to cause us pain for days to come at the slightest movement.

They laced us up into a tight package and placed us on the ground near the edge of the plateau, about fifty meters from their camping ground. Now I observed that they were familiar after all with the art of making fire. They lit fire close in front of their caves and fed it with a few branches and twigs they seemed to have carried up here with them from the plains. Up here, snow had already fallen. Nothing grew.

My glance kept wandering again and again down to the high plain, but if the adjutant's glider was really flying there to search for us, I could hardly have detected it against the irregular pattern of the background. I guessed that we had climbed up the mountain to an altitude of nearly 4,500 meters. The air was thin and icy cold. I now began to experience vivid pangs of hunger and terrible thirst. Woefully, I was thinking of the last drop of whiskey that had vanished together with my knapsack and my checkbook.

Toward noon, Thomé nudged me as best he could under the circumstances. "Just keep lying there, Walter. Don't budge! The glider is approaching from over there. The wild bunch hasn't discovered it yet."

"And what if he doesn't discover us either?"

"Don't worry, he will! This mountaintop is too conspicuous to overlook. The adjutant knows these savages. Besides, he has to cross this plateau if he wants to get to the valley on the other side of this mountain. Listen closely, Walter: as soon as the glider is flying over us here, its appearance in the sky is bound to attract the attention of the savages. We'll stand up then, so the adjutant can see us. Too bad we can't wave."

By now I could make out the glider. Slowly and soundlessly it flew along the rocky path we had stumbled up yesterday, flying very close to the ground. I was certain the pilot would see our tracks.

The cannibals spotted the glider and began to yell.

Supporting each other, back to back, we managed to get to our feet, swaying unsteadily. We could not move our feet to keep our balance—but we were standing upright. The pilot had to see us.

The savages jumped to their feet. Some ran panic-stricken, to vanish inside the caves that dotted the hillside. Others remained stockstill, paralyzed by fear. And not until the glider came down for a landing did they, too, take to their heels.

The adjutant climbed out of the open cockpit and walked over to where we were standing. With an almost indulgent smile he took a small steel knife from his pocket and cut our bonds. Later on, Thomé translated for me the conversation that took place between the two.

"You were very lucky, you know, to be still alive. The natives will always kill any captives they take, and as a rule they will do this right away. Why didn't you listen to my advice? I told you how dangerous it is these days to venture out alone in these mountains."

"Everything turned out all right, adjutant," replied Thomé without the least trace of embarrassment. "We feel very much obliged to you. Are we going to remain a while longer here in Tiahuanacu?"

"No, we are flying straight back to Cuzco. Your adventure must not interfere with our plans—you'll understand that, I'm sure."

"Our friend here," Thomé pointed to me, "has lost his knapsack during this incident. He carried in it many important items he cannot do without."

"I'll give instructions for a search. Now please get in."

Thomé whispered to me that any further attempt to urge the adjutant to remain in the area would have caused suspicion. For the time being, therefore, my knapsack was lost, and the sphinx was stuck in the "keyhole" of a secret chamber near Tiahuanacu. I would have to try and get it back as soon as possible.

We flew back to Cuzco. Despite the fact that my life was no longer endangered, I did not feel any too happy.

During the flight our adjutant was very tight-lipped. I wondered if this was because of the time he had lost on our adventure. But as soon as we reached Cuzco, I began to understand why he was so unusually sullen.

The savages had made an attack on the plateau near Cuzco. The attack had been easily repelled, without energy weapons. Dead savages were scattered all over, their wounds giving mute testimony to how they had met their end. The Altairians had set their invulnerable robots against them. Energy weapons and laser guns, especially on this unprotected, open plateau, would have alerted the control base in Europe. Since the Altairians did not know how to handle effectively the natives' spears and clubs, only the robots remained to ward off the attackers. The machine men were not bothered by even the most powerful blows. The savages must have been terrified when they faced the invincible, shining metal men, whom they had known thus far only as obedient laborers.

Back in my apartment I attacked the food set out for me like a hungry wolf. After my meal I decided to visit Thomé and talk him into flying back to Tiahuanacu with me the next day. It would be easy to find some pretext for returning there without letting the Altairians know the real reason for this trip.

I must get the sphinx back into my possession!

But everything turned out quite different than I had planned.

Thomé was sitting in an armchair, staring at the ceiling, when I entered. "Have a seat; that's better. To-morrow you will have to travel back to your own time. Orders of the commander, Walter."

I sat down abruptly. "Tomorrow morning? Why so suddenly?"

He shrugged his shoulders. "An attack by the natives is expected, this time on a far larger scale. Everything is being readied for the defense of the plateau. The Altairians don't want you exposed to danger, so they insist on your early departure."

"Do you believe this is the real reason?"

"Maybe. In any case, you won't be able to get your sphinx back, or your knapsack."

"And what am I supposed to tell Erich?"

Thomé looked at me with a piercing glance, then folded his hands and inspected his fingernails.

"Don't say anything to him. As soon as you arrive back in the future, travel from Cuzco to Tiahuanacu. Get yourself a horse or a donkey and ride to the cave where we were ambushed. In the chamber at the end of the narrow passage you'll stop, bend down, and pull the sphinx out of the rock. Then you'll return to Europe and give Erich the sphinx." An enigmatic smile played around his lips as he continued: "You see, it's as simple as that."

I kept staring at him. It took a while for me to comprehend what he had said.

"You can't believe that the figure will remain undetected inside this cave for twenty-three thousand years?"

He rested his elbows on the table. "I have given this a good deal of thought. Just as there are two time machines in existence—the *same* time machine twice, in different time planes—there must also exist two absolutely identical stone figures. Maybe even three. For after all, I found it in the pyramid above Sacsayhuaman thirty years before you'll find it in Tiahuanacu. Don't ask me to explain how such a thing can be possible. I don't know the answer. It's probably connected with two different probability dimensions which exist simultaneously side by side. It's possible to shift from one to the other without even noticing it. Do you follow me?"

I nodded my head, though I understood nothing at all of what he tried to explain to me. I only knew that his assumption must be working somehow. And if it did work, then I incurred no risk in setting out tomorrow morning on my journey back to the twentieth century A.D. Not even if I arrived minus my checkbook: Jacques Ferrant would certainly advance me the money to travel to Tiahuanacu and then back to Europe.

"But one thing, Professor Thomé—how will I get out of the secret chamber? I must have the sphinx to activate the opening mechanism!"

"No problem, Walter. Don't forget that I handed Erich von X. my own stone figure when we met in Egypt. Which meant I had to first have a second key made for me. I never used this second key, because I found the genuine companion-piece that time in Egypt—as expected. When I came here I brought along the second key—and you can have it."

A crafty look crept into his eyes. He crawled under his bed and dragged out an ancient looking suitcase from underneath. Hidden among all kinds of trash stemming from the twentieth century A.D., lay the duplicate sphinx. It was made of white plaster of paris.

He handed it to me.

"Well, it's agreed then, Professor Thomé. I'll leave you tomorrow. You were a great help to me, Professor. Depend on it, I'll bring your manuscript safely to Switzerland and give it to Erich. I won't leave your papers out of my sight, till I hand them over to Erich in person."

"Please, do exactly that!" he said seriously. "If my manuscript should fall into the wrong hands, all would have been in vain. Incredible as it might sound, I wouldn't put it past the Altairian control base to interfere. And they have some fantastic means at their disposal.

"Many an explorer or research scientist has found out too much for his own good—and talked about his findings. As a consequence, many an explorer has vanished without a trace. The difference, Walter, is that these poor vanished people did not have a time machine they could use like I did."

We sat together in his room for nearly five hours discussing the multitude of topics that preoccupied our minds. Among the things we talked about was the subject of telepathy.

"What about the so-called voices Erich used to hear whenever you tried to establish contact with him?" I asked him. "Not that I doubt that they exist, for I had a similar experience. Do you believe there is such a thing as telepathy?"

"Yes, I do—in this relatively undeveloped form. After all, we make no use of the major part of our brain; this is a well-established fact. We do not know the purpose of that section which is lying idle. There are two possibilities: once upon a time man's brain was developed to its optimum extent, and humans possessed all psi factors. Then man managed to destroy himself and his civilization with these special abilities. Now, however, we know that this was not what happened. Therefore we must assume that the other alternative is correct: the brain has not yet reached its full potential. We are only at the beginning of our development; we are nothing but a transitory stage. Someday in the future, homo sapiens will represent the existing link to homo superior, who will be able to utilize his total brain potential. It's quite likely, however, that already today some brains have reached a more advanced stage. I wouldn't go so far as to call them mutants. These few specially gifted people have an inkling of what man-after-man will be able to accomplish—provided mankind survives long enough to reach that goal. They feel it in their subconscious mind. They can receive thoughts as long as they are broadcast with a conscious and powerful effort. Just as I had been seeking Erich von X. without knowing him. And he *had* to receive my mental messages because we are both on the same frequency."

He fell silent for a few moments, gazing calmly and deeply into my eyes, before he added in a particularly serious tone of voice: "I even wonder whether it might not be due to the control base of the Altairians here on Earth that suddenly various individuals are setting out on a search for the 'gods from the stars.' And furthermore, that all these people are unknowingly but evidently maintaining some contact with each other."

The notion was shocking, but I felt fascinated by it at the same time. Could a machine broadcast impulses that certain brains would respond to? Thomé, Pauwels, and Bergier; Charroux, I, and Erich? If we located this station—what then? I tried to put these thoughts out of my mind and turned again to Thomé. "What is your opinion about the time machine? Who do you think constructed it and left it in these caves?"

"I am almost certain that it originates in the future —*our own* future. A few things speak against this assumption, I'll admit. For if somebody in our future invented such an instrument, then there ought to be more than one. We should by now have received some visitors from the future. There is no proof that this has happened—although there are certain incidents."

"What incidents?"

"Nothing definite, Walter. But sometimes things happen in our world that can be explained only by the secret emergence of time travelers from the future on the one hand, and on the other hand by the gentle action of memory molecules which are present in the human body and which have existed in us since time immemorial. These molecules were passed on from generation to generation, losing nothing of their memory retention power. This latter theory would of course necessitate the previous existence here on Earth of a civilization far superior to our own—and I'm no longer inclined to believe that this was ever the case." He paused for a moment, then continued: "Let's consider the case of Leonardo da Vinci. A highly talented man, a genius. But how did he become a genius? Remembering the past? Or remembering his own future?"

It was approximately 10 o'clock—by my own watch that I had never changed—when I took my leave. Contented, yet at the same time nervous and excited, I returned to my apartment. Tomorrow I would say good-bye to the commander and the adjutant prior to setting out on the return trip to my own era. Many a mystery I could now check off my list as being solved. But there remained a whole slew of new problems to be answered.

* * *

The next morning Professor Thomé and the adjutant brought me back to the crystal labyrinth and the time machine. I had no luggage any more, except for the professor's manuscript and the plaster-of-paris sphinx. I had stowed away the manuscript between my shirt and pullover for safety.

We hardly spoke. When we arrived on the plateau I noticed more robots there than usual. They did no work; instead, they were doing guard duty. It appeared, indeed, as if they were awaiting any moment now an attack by the natives.

We found the time machine all intact in the secret chamber.

Thomé spoke to me in English: "Don't forget what I have tried to impress on you: Once you arrive again in the future, leave the time machine, insert the figure into the 'keyhole,' and wait until the separating wall descends into the floor. From the moment that the upper edge of this wall is level with the threshold on the ground, you'll have exactly thirty seconds till the door will close again. That will leave you sufficient time to get out of the secret chamber, buy don't dawdle and waste any time by looking around or trying to take something with you from the chamber. Is that understood?"

I nodded.

Now the adjutant shook my hand and wished me good luck. Then he stepped back to make room for the professor, who in turn took leave of me.

"Give my most affectionate and cordial regards to Erich. Let him write his book now, but it would be very good if he could get himself together to undertake a trip. He ought to have a good look at the places he is writing about. And if he is short of money, he should borrow some. He'll soon be able to repay his debt tenfold. And please bear in mind under all circumstances: neither you nor Erich may journey back into the past before your year 1968, and in no case must the time machine be used again *after* 1972. Don't *ever* forget that, Walter!"

"The machine will function only seven more years without endangering our lives . . . it's hard to believe. I'll warn Erich, rest assured."

"Fine. And now—" he firmly squeezed my hand —"keep a stiff upper lip and good luck to you." I entered the cage and sat down on the chair. The lamps began to glow, as Thomé added: "Push the lever all the way up, all at once. That's all you need do. Good-bye!"

I put the little package with the plaster-of-paris figure on the floor of the cabin, then seized the lever. From beneath my seat I could hear the hum of the mysterious energy supply of the time machine.

Then I followed the professor's instructions. I

pushed the lever upward with one firm, steady movement until it engaged with an audible click.

The mists of the time stream began to envelop me, and with unimaginable speed I was rushing toward the future till I caught up with it . . .

six

As I emerged from the half-demolished passage into the open air, the hot rays of the midday sun beat directly into my face. A swift look around assured me that I had indeed returned to my own time. There was the dilapidated pyramid, higher up the weatherbeaten entrance to the blocked-up crystal labyrinth; down below, the threefold staggered wall of the fortress at Sacsayhuaman.

Everything had gone off perfectly—almost!

As the mists of time began to lift again, I instinctively picked the little package with the imitation sphinx off the floor, and hastily tore off the wrapping paper. I still found enough nerve to shut the door of the time-machine cage. Then I flipped on the little lamp Thomé had given me and shoved the plaster-of-paris figure into the keyhole. The barrier wall started to descend. I kept thinking of the barely thirty seconds remaining to me; nervously, I pulled at the figure's tail, then tried to yank it out of the hole—

And then it broke!

There was no time for manipulations. The wall was already rising again from the floor. I dove out into the main corridor, landing hard on the floor. The light

141

of the small, high-intensity lamp Thomé had given me went out.

It was difficult finding my way out to the exit without any light, but I managed. I breathed a deep sigh of relief when I saw daylight ahead at the end of the passageway.

And now I was standing outside under the open sky.

I was once more in the year 1965!

I wondered how Erich had fared, in the meantime. I could picture very vividly his restlessness, his impatient waiting for the outcome of my mission. As soon as Ferrant loaned me the money, I would send a cable to my friend in Switzerland. After that, Tiahuanacu, to fetch my sphinx. Then, finally, I would be ready to fly back to Europe.

But once again everything turned out quite different than planned . . .

The walk down to the high plateau was easy. I passed by the old Inca fortress, regarding it now with quite different eyes than when I first saw it with Ferrant, not so long ago. There were a few tourists about. They did not bother me when I took a closer look at the gigantic stone wall, which rose for many meters in front of me. The huge blocks were piled on top of each other without visible seams or joints—still a mystery for scientists. But now I knew how these blocks had come to be. Of course, the Altairians themselves would never have bothered erecting walls with them. That had been work for the Incas. It would not have been a very difficult task, for the large amounts of debris, huge rock chunks carted out from the crystal labyrinth under construction, were lying scattered all over the plateau.

I took a tourist taxi; I did not want to encounter so many people. The driver asked no questions. He probably thought I was a tourist who had lost his way. I did not mention Ferrant's name; I wanted to make sure he did not know my destination. He would certainly have understood that name, even though I could not speak Spanish.

He let me off in front of the Hotel Savoy, a few hundred meters from the football stadium.

My little package jammed under my right arm, I kept marching, looking forward to the tasty meal the old Indian woman would cook for us.

I arrived at the house surrounded by the high wall, climbed up on the big stone, and rang the bell. It took a long time until the little hatch opened.

It wasn't Ferrant's eye that stared at me. It was the Indian woman.

She recognized me immediately and opened the gate. Hardly had the door closed again behind us than she broke out in tears, loosing a flood of words upon me. Naturally I failed to understand a single word. Suddenly she seized my arm and led me into the house. I began rehearsing my few words of French, hardly more than her own, prepared for a difficult conversation.

Ferrant seemed not to be at home. Had he left on a trip? Was he in Cuzco?

"Il est mort!"

It took nearly three seconds till the words were absorbed by my conscious mind. Totally bewildered, I stared into the furrowed face, which seemed to have aged by many years.

"Ferrant is dead?"

She nodded her head. She understood my miserable French.

"Dead? How did this happen?"

"He became ill, then he died. That's all. Two weeks ago." It was inconceivable that this should have happened. Not that I had a very close relationship with Ferrant—I hardly knew the man. But since I had lost my checkbook and my airplane ticket, he represented the only way for me to get back to Europe. Where else could I obtain the money I needed? Who in Europe even would cable my return fare?

The Indian woman stammered in a weird mixture of French and English: "He left a letter for you. Wait, I'll get it."

I was at the end of my wits. My expectation of a tasty meal had completely vanished; I felt leaden emptiness in my stomach. Without asking for permission, I went to the sideboard and poured myself a stiff drink.

There *must* be a way out of this damned situation. I would certainly find it!

The Indian woman returned and handed me a thick, sealed envelope. Then she said: *"Voilà!* I'm going to prepare your room and your dinner."

She disappeared before I had time to answer.

Puzzled, I held the envelope in my hand. The crazy thought that it might contain some money lasted barely a second. Why should Ferrant leave money for me? Everything indicated that he had never possessed a lot of it.

I hastily tore open the envelope. It contained some ten typewritten pages, stapled together, and a single sheet of paper addressed to me.

I began to read:

Dear Mr. Ernsting!

Sorry I won't be here when you return. Maybe you'll never return. In that case no one will ever read this letter, for I have left instructions with Huamaca to destroy it exactly one year after my death. I enclose a report for Erich von X. Please see to it that he gets it. This report contains the details of my last meeting with Thomé before he vanished forever. The pistol—you know what I mean—lies down at the bottom of the well. I thought it too risky to leave it behind.

A few more days, and my life will be be over. Nobody can help me. Farewell, and all the best of luck to you and to your friend. You'll need it.

The pain is becoming unbearable, my friend. Thank your Creator if some day you're permitted to die a swift and unexpected death. Nothing is worse than to be condemned to die and find out about it in time. Don't we all refuse to accept the judgment imposed on us from the day we were born? When the gods created man they decreed his final destiny to be death. They reserved immortality for themselves—thus it is written by Gilgamesh. I am eager to find out what will happen after the cells of my body have died. Perhaps we'll all meet again in the so-called beyond.

Yours
Jacques Ferrant

Considerably shaken, I put the letter back into the envelope together with Ferrant's report. Since I always try to keep all important papers in one place, I added Thomé's manuscript.

Huamaca, the old Indian woman, served dinner. I did not feel very hungry but I had to eat something. After all, I hadn't taken any nourishment for 23,000 years!

After dinner I asked her to open the safe for me to take out my passport. It was the only document I had deposited there before I journeyed into the past. I was cursing myself for having dragged along my checkbook and airplane ticket in my knapsack. But then I comforted myself with the thought that my situation would be so much worse now if I had also lost my passport. You may be forgiven for having no money. But with no passport you are as good as dead.

Later that night, when I was stretched out in bed and the creeping cold could still be felt even under the warm blankets, I began to ponder seriously my situation. No doubt about it, I was in a fix! Without a single cent in my pocket, I was sitting here in Cuzco, some 10,000 kilometers from home. The only person I knew here who could have helped me was dead. I didn't know a single other soul in South America.

South America is a huge continent, unimaginably wild and in certain ways also immeasurably rich. But there was nobody in it who would lend me the money for my flight back to Europe.

My return flight ticket had as its starting point Lima, capital city of Peru. My first problem was now how to get to Lima. First, making a detour via Tiahuanacu was out of question now. My immediate goal was Lima. Once there, I would find some solution to this dilemna . . .

Lima—!

Somewhere in my tortured brain clicked a memory relay. There was something in connection with Lima . . . a name . . . a person. I had no idea who that might be, I only knew: Lima was the key! In Lima I would find some solution to this catastrophe.

I can't remember now how long I was tossing in my bed, searching my brain in vain, trying to reconstruct what I expected to find in Lima.

Later on, I often wondered why we sometimes become so forgetful. I had a friend in Salzburg with whom I used to talk for hours about lost cultures and vanished tribes. He knew about my meeting with Erich von X., and he was highly enthusiastic about my trip to South America. He envied me for this chance, but he was a doctor and his profession left him little time for personal leisure.

While I lay sleepless in my bed in Cuzco, I recalled what my friend Andreas Kofol had told me: "South America is a land full of surprises. Peru, most of all Peru! You may encounter difficulties, Walter, serious trouble. I have a cousin living in Lima; go to him if you need help. Just tell him you are my friend, and he'll do for you whatever he can. He is a very sensitive, generous, wonderful guy. Write down his address. He is a professor of Indian studies—he spent seven years in India, where he studied Sanskrit, the holy language. He attempts to establish a casual connection between the cultures of Peru and India! He is convinced that once there was a direct link between the Andes and Angkor, the grandiose ruins in Indo-China. He's the right man for you to contact!"

The name! I absolutely couldn't recall his name. I hadn't written it down, despite my friend's urging, for I was convinced I couldn't forget such a name. It was such a simple name . . . just an ordinary Spanish man's name.

Juan?

No, something like that maybe . . . José perhaps . . .

Of course, José!

And the rest of his name? His family name?

I had now at least one difinite lead: Kofol, Lima, and José. I turned over on my other side. That should do it for today.

It shouldn't be too difficult to track down in Lima a professor of Indiology whose first name was José.

He was probably around forty years of age.

I must find him!

My immediate problem, though, was how to get to Lima?

That night I slept very fitfully. How different I had imagined my return to the present would be! I had just lived through an adventure more fantastic than anybody could ever dream of—and here I was, now, sitting penniless in a medium-sized city, in the middle of the Andes, bringing back with me an incredible sounding report and a stone from the past.

At least the stone wasn't entirely ordinary. It had broken off from one of the huge rock chunks as it was rolled down the hill by the Altairian laborers. Just an ordinary piece of rock—except for a few square centimeters. This particular spot still showed evidence that it had recently been cut with laser beams.

León!

That was the family name! It suddenly dawned on me as the first sun's rays fell into the room through the wide-open windows.

Professor José de León in Lima!

I jumped out of bed. All I needed now was his exact address. If I'd read it, I was sure to remember it; that was no problem.

Huamaca had breakfast ready for me. I asked her to sit down with me at the table. Very hesitantly she accepted my invitation. She was apparently not accustomed to sitting at the same table as her employer.

Well, I wasn't her employer. I felt much more like a humble person about to ask a great favor.

"How can I get to Lima?" I wanted to know from her.

There was no direct train between Cuzco and Lima. I had to travel first to Huancavelica along a road about 400 kilometers straight across through the Andes. There was a railroad station with connections to Lima, about another 380 kilometers. Again the painful question: where would I find the money for this trip!

Huamaca looked at me in surprise.

"Lima? That's where your airplane is waiting? But we also have airplanes here!"

The old lady had a sense of humor! I would have preferred if she had had some money instead. Of course, there were lots of airplanes waiting in Cuzco and in Lima—but not for one without money. I tried to make her understand my situation. She looked at me for a long time, thinking hard; then her face suddenly lit up.

"One of my uncles often drives to Lima. He could give you a lift."

"Without any money?"

"Doesn't matter. He transports metal loads in a big truck." She looked at me with appraising eyes. "You don't weigh much."

"Where does your uncle live, Huamaca?"

"In Cuzco. We'll pay him a visit."

This was my first opportunity to get to see something of Cuzco at last, although I must admit in all honesty that I was never especially tempted to sightsee, however beautiful and interesting a place might be. Cuzco had approximately 100,000 inhabitants and scarcely reminded one of the old realm of the Incas. Time and earthquakes, and above all the Spanish invaders driven by lust for conquest, had eradicated most of the traces of a glorious past. Fortunately they had not succeeded everywhere.

Huamaca's uncle had a business transporting goods from Cuzco either to the railroad station in Huancavelica, where they were loaded on freight trains, or directly to Lima. He was scheduled to deliver a load to Lima in a couple of days. I explained my misfortune to him. When he heard from his niece that I had been a friend of Ferrant's, he invited me to be his travel companion.

He was certainly not older than Huamaca, and I could not make out what their family relationship actually was. In any case, he promised to pick me up in two days at six o'clock in the morning at Ferrant's house.

Thus I would pass the first hurdle in my obstacle race to get back to Europe. I was quite pleased as Huamaca and I returned to the orphaned home of the eccentric French professor. The only thing that rankled now was the fact that I had to forego a detour to Tiahuanacu, but I realized how fortunate I was even to be able to get to Lima under the circumstances. After all, if the sphinx had lasted 23,000 years in that cave, one more year would make no difference.

I spent the next day making an excursion into the city's environs, but the only things that still retained some resemblance to the landscape as it was at the time of the Altairians were the snow-covered, eternal mountaintops of the Andes. At least they had survived these many thousands of years undamaged.

The following morning I was awakened by Huamaca, and a short while later her uncle came driving along, honking his horn as if he wanted to wake up the entire city. I took my bundle with manuscripts, the stone and a few provisions, jingled the few coins that were a gift from Huamaca, gave the old lady a hearty kiss on her wrinkled cheek, and ran out of the house.

The huge truck began to move slowly, its exhaust pipe sounding like a stuttering machine gun.

I was on my way.

* * *

I could tell a great deal about the magnificent sights nature had to offer during our drive to Lima, but it is not the purpose of this report to describe the beauties of nature in these parts of the world. The unique scenery which reminds one of paradise and hell simultaneously. The fertile valleys with their settlements, the isolated high plateaus enclosed by steep rock walls and mountaintops, the narrow mountain passes and the bottomless abysses between impassable cliffs—they all left in me an overwhelming impression. I love solitude without ever feeling quite at ease in it. The Andes, not to be compared with the European Alps, *are* a very lonely place.

This is where man arrived last.

Huamina! Ayacucho! Huancavelica!

The railroad line began here. Huamaca's uncle, whose name I don't recall any longer, gave me to understand that from now on, also, the overland road would become better. The road ran parallel to the railroad tracks for long stretches at a time, then we were again separated from the tracks, as they sought the shortest path through the mountains by crossing over vertiginous wooden bridges.

Two days later we arrived in Lima.

There was a brief but cordial farewell scene from the old Indian. I expressed my gratitude and promised to return someday. On that occasion, I assured him, I would belatedly pay for my share of the travel expenses —a promise that Erich von X. made good for me later on.

Well, here I was now, in the middle of an unknown big city, with practically no money and only one name in my possession. I had to find a phonebook.

There were no public phone booths in sight, but I had hardly taken twenty paces when I stumbled over some steps leading up to the entrance to a post office.

However, I had not taken into account that the name León occurs in South America with about the same frequency as the name Smith in the United States or the name Schmitz in Germany. There was also a whole long list of Josés, but thank goodness only one professor of Indian culture.

Canevaro 157 . . .

I decided against phoning my friend's relative. It

would be easier to take care of the matter in person.
Besides, I could not know if whoever answered the
phone would understand English or German.

I quickly found León's house, and soon met him
face to face.

At first I was startled by his appearance. What I
saw here was a regular Spanish conquistador from the
eighteenth century. His complexion had a greenish-
yellow tinge like an olive, his hair was smooth and
black, his figure small and very slender, almost grace-
ful.

Haltingly I explained that I was a friend of his
cousin in Austria. Immediately, he acted more friendly; little did he know what the actual purpose of my
visit was! When he asked me to stay for dinner I decided to postpone the moment when I would put the
touch on him. Otherwise, it would surely spoil all our
appetites.

We finished our meal and then my host took me to
his study. He looked me straight in the eye and said in
a polite and pleasant manner: "I believe you are in a
tight spot. How can I help you?"

I simply nodded. "It's true, but how did you
know? Did I put on such a bad show?"

"You seemed to be insecure, and I noticed this.
Do you need any money?"

Without divulging where and *when* I had been, I
told him about my bad luck in losing my cash, checkbook, and airplane ticket. He listened to my tale and
only occasionally interrupted me with catch questions
which I did not really take amiss.

"How is Andy?" he would ask casually. "Still involved in that useless business of being a radio ham?"

I simply remarked that his cousin could barely
distinguish a transistor from a straight pin.

"And how about his delicate little daughter Annette—still in poor health?"

I protested. Annette was anything but delicate or
sickly, quite the contrary.

"And how are things with Rosy, Andy's mother?"

"Her name is Emma," I informed him. "And she's still crazy about Maxi, whom I'm supposed to resemble quite a bit."

José de León gave a reserved smile. "I see you are well-informed. Only a few people know about her preference for Maxi. All right, how much money do you need?"

To make a long story short, he arranged for my flight tickets, paid for everything, and even invited me to spend the night in his house till it would be time to leave to catch the plane to Bogotá. After dinner, José de León invited me to join him again in his study. He discussed his research work. I could easily have given him a few tips, but I was bound by my word of honor. Of course there was a connection between the cultures of South America and India! But it dated back much farther than León suspected. I would gladly have told him about it in order to repay him for his generous help, but then I would have had to give him a complete account of what had happened to me—and that was impossible.

This hospitable family couldn't do enough for me. They outfitted me with a new, lightweight suit, made in Peru, and presented me with a well-filled air-flight bag. It contained Peruvian perfumes and embroideries for the ladies at home, besides my documents and the small stone from the past. They asked me to transmit all kinds of messages and greetings to the family in Salzburg. And a lot of kisses from José for Emma.

My flight led me first from Lima to Bogotá via Braniff Airlines. In Bogotá I changed planes and flew with Air France to Rio de Janeiro, Dakar, and Paris. For a change they were striking again in Paris; half the scheduled flights had been canceled, and I was lucky to catch a BEA plane to London.

My aversion to flying in commercial airplanes is quite well-known to all my friends. This does not apply, though, to the small, easily maneuverable sports machines which—I have been told again and again—can still safely land in some field in case of engine trouble. But whenever I'm sitting in such a flying autobus, I'm always overcome by the unpleasant sensation of being locked inside a death cell. Just the fact of being so high above the ground, without a parachute on hand, evokes in me the most horrible visions. In addition, the prospect of arriving perhaps in Cuba instead of London was anything but enticing. These fears are mostly unfounded, but unfortunately I'm prey to them.

London!

What a marvelous opportunity to stop over and visit my friend Carnell in Plumstead. He had no idea of my recent experiences, and as usual our conversation was limited to purely business affairs. We were both literary agents, specializing in science fiction, and had many business dealings with each other. Later that evening the topic of our conversation turned to the theoretical possibility of a time machine. I had to restrain myself hard from letting on too much; it would have been so easy to prove him wrong. But I was in no position to indulge myself in telling what I really knew.

Frankfurt!

Munich!

And then at last: Irschenberg in Upper Bavaria, home again!

My wife was already expecting me since I had changed my original plan to fly directly to Zürich. After all, Christmas was near at hand, and I'd been away for close to three months. One more week wouldn't make any difference now.

Besides, this would leave me some time for putting my notes in order, to read over Thomé's report at leisure, and study Ferrant's letter to Erich, which contained nothing new. I had long since sent a telegram to Davos, and on December 23 a reply arrived:

"Expect you between Christmas and New Year's. Erich."

My wife tried to squeeze me like a lemon that isn't quite ripe yet. She didn't get much out of me. She is a sober, matter-of-fact person, and I didn't dare share the story of the time machine with her. Not only would she have laughed at me, but she would have considered me crazy. So I told her about marvelous excursions into the mountain world of Peru, of imaginary adventures with rapacious highway robbers, of Ferrant and his old Indian servant, and of my stay in Lima with the hospitable León family.

In between, I drove to Salzburg and gave Andreas money to transfer to his cousin José on my behalf. He was the only person who learned the whole truth before I had a chance to tell it to Erich. Andreas believed me and could keep his mouth shut. Furthermore, he regarded the existence of an Altairian control base in our own time as not only possible but also highly probable and logical.

"They certainly have a plan stretching over thousands of years. Why should they ever have abandoned it? They are here on Earth! Perhaps in the Vatican, perhaps in the U.N. What do *we* know? There are too many things in our time, especially political or religious events, which can't be explained away. Why do you think this isn't possible? The extraterrestrials are sitting in key political and religious positions—and they don't want a peaceful solution."

"For heaven's sake!" I exclaimed. "That sounds like a plot for a TV series!"

"Thank goodness, nobody will believe me. *But you know it!*"

If such an Altairian 100,000-year plan really did exist, what was its purpose? Not to destroy us, that is obvious. No senseless invasion. Rather, to watch over our progress toward a global socialism which eventually will result in that stage of maturity which is the indispensable prerequisite for our acceptance into the Galactic Federation. Mankind, meanwhile having become highly developed, was not to be united by forceful threats or wars. The human race must climb up this path to maturity all alone, under its own power. With their superior technological means it would be child's play for the members of the Galactic Federation to enforce everlasting worldwide peace in a single day. But this would mean interference in the course of natural evolution, which was strictly forbidden. Thus they were forced to watch with their hands tied while one nation after another created its own nuclear weapons, disrupting the balance of fear. It was quite clear. As soon as nuclear warfare broke out, the work of the Galactic Federation here on Earth would come to an end.

Or might they start all over again?

Three days after Christmas, I parked my car below the Hotel Rosehill in Davos. The bellboy carried my suitcase to a prebooked room, and a little later there came an energetic knock on the door.

I greeted my friend with open arms, but he scarcely shook my hand—as though we had said good-bye one hour ago and not almost nine months. I realized Erich's odd behavior had nothing to do with rudeness or lack of friendly feelings toward me personally. Anyone who knows Erich von X. is aware that this man is ruled by one idea. He can't be bothered for a second with any of the niceties which the rest of us take for granted.

"Great, you're back! What's the news? Hurry up, and let me hear your story!"

I shook my head and sat down. His gaze wandered around the room, stopped on my suitcase which was still standing on a chair. "Did you bring back anything? How about the time machine? Were you in the past—or not?"

"Have a seat first!" I entreated him and waited until, quite impatient and nervous, he followed my advice. "I will tell you the whole story in the proper sequence. But right away I want you to know: The time machine does exist! I traveled to the past. Well! Do you feel any better now?"

He just stared at me. Then: "Man, is that the truth?" His question revealed quite plainly to me how he had been swaying between belief and disbelief for a full decade. "Get going, Walter! Let me hear!"

I told my tale.

One hour later, when I started getting hoarse, Erich ordered a bottle of wine. I was very grateful for the wine and the brief intermission, but fortunately he let me tell my story otherwise without any interruptions. He asked no questions but looked at me with steadfast eyes. I felt as if his gaze was penetrating into the innermost hidden recesses of my soul. This man, I realized, would never fall victim to a lie. But I didn't care; for I told him the full truth with every little detail.

Not until I mentioned the loss of the sphinx did his behavior change. A look of horror came into his eyes and he gasped: "You don't have it anymore? Good God—!"

"I'm sorry. It was impossible to rescue it. Thomé and I didn't dare arouse the suspicions of the Altairians, under any circumstances. They knew that I had the sphinx in my possession, but we could not let them find out that we planned to enter the other secret chamber. The figure is still where we left it in Tiahuanacu, I'm sure."

It did not take long to tell the rest. I gave him Thomé's report and Ferrant's farewell letter. While he was reading them, very excited and rather quickly (which I could fully appreciate, because he'd have plenty of time later on for a thorough study of these papers), I took the stone from my suitcase and put it on the table. Contrary to my original intention to keep it as a souvenir for myself, I had brought it along for Erich. It was supposed to furnish the final proof, even if Thomé's manuscript, signed by the professor to authenticate its contents, was not sufficient in itself.

"That's to make up for the lost sphinx?"

He picked up the stone and examined it. He noticed the glazed spot and ran his fingertips over the tiny, smooth expanse. Then he looked at me. "Well, well. The crystal labyrinth. The answer to all the questions scientists have posed about how the Incas achieved such an incredible degree of workmanship and artistic skill! Cut with laser rays, exposed to wind and weather for more than 20,000 years—and the results are the amazingly exact stone blocks of the temples, fortresses, and walls of the Incas." He smiled for the first time that day. "Yes, indeed. Now we have proof in our hands that everything really was that way.

But do you actually believe we could convince the public with these facts? Never, absolutely not! But nobody can hold me back from expounding my theories, even if I have to do it without furnishing tangible proof. *I* have the evidence. That's enough for me. It supplies me with the necessary support, so I'll be able to debate these theories with any doubting Thomas. It'll infuse me with strength to face the criticism and derision of the scientists. I needed these proofs for the strength of inner conviction. Do you understand that?"

Indeed I could empathize with Erich!

"Will you go to Peru . . . I mean soon?" I asked.

He shrugged his shoulders. "That damned hotel . . . ! When I took over that place it was heavily in debt —and I haven't managed yet to get rid of it. As far as monetary matters are concerned—as you've found out by now—I'm a big, fat zero. I've borrowed some money, though, and have invested it in the hotel, and I'm sure it's going uphill from now on."

"You shouldn't borrow money on your hotel. Borrow some on your book," I suggested. "Thomé is convinced the book will bring you a lot of money if it's properly written—and the sample you let me read last spring was written very well indeed. Don't make the mistake of presenting your theories in too dry and purely scientific a manner. Nobody will bother reading such stuff. Write in a lively, challenging, provocative style! Pose questions to the reader. Involve him. Have him think along with you. Point him in the direction that will automatically lead him to draw his own conclusions. Never say that things took place in such and such a way! Always write that it *could* have happened in that manner!"

"I would have done that anyway, even if I hadn't known the truth," he remarked. "I'll confront the public with a flood of questions. And as to the style . . ."

"Don't worry about that, Erich. We have editors who get paid to doctor a manuscript so it's ready to go to press. Good editors and proofreaders remain as faithful as possible to the writer's original work; they just polish it and check once in a while in a dictionary or

other style reference books. That's all. What you have
to say will remain unchanged, and in your particular
case you should use a popular style. Even so, I'd suggest
that you first take that trip. Only if you've seen everything with your own eyes can you judge properly—and
ask questions. The *right* questions! It was most peculiar
how dead-sure Thomé was that this book would make
you rich."

"He was, really?" Erich laughed, and raised his
glass in a toast: "Let's hope the gods will grant him that
prediction! I'll drink to that!"

I remained serious. "The gods, at least those who
wield power today, will be the last to be willing to help
you . . ."

* * *

I stayed a couple of days in Davos, then returned
to my family, to resume my usual work. I had left the
stone for Erich as a replacement for the lost sphinx.
There was no way for me to lend him some money; I
had hardly anything left in my bank account. It was
high time to settle down and write some novels to tide
us over this period. I could not help him as much as I'd
have liked to do. But he assured me I needn't worry,
he'd get the money somehow. And next fall he'd be
ready to start out on his trip. The first draft of his book
would be ready by then.

Many things changed in my life that year also.

My family and I left Irschenberg with a heavy
heart and moved to Salzburg. There were many reasons
that spoke in favor of such a move. It had no bad effect
on my work, which I kept up without interruption in
order to make a living. Unfortunately, that was about all
I got out of my writing. I would dearly have loved to
accompany Erich on his journey to South America. But
it was impossible.

From time to time I received a letter from Erich. It
usually dealt with "our topic," bringing new insights and
explanations for events taking place daily in our world,
only to be forgotten a few days later by the rest of the

people. Through Erich, I saw that they were important
and unequivocal indications for *us* of the continued
existence of the Altairian control station. An additional
reason to remain cautious! Looked at in this light, we
were already in a dilemna in 1966.

Spring and summer 1966 passed without any note-
worthy events. Erich prepared for his journey on the
QT. I had not the faintest idea how he proposed to fi-
nance this trip. There are detailed reports about this
elsewhere; I am not referring here, though, to those
which later on were published in the legal records of
our courts of law. The latter are crammed full of false
assertions, accusations, insinuations—as I know today
with certainty.

It is hardly necessary to give a detailed account
here of Erich's first trip to South America. I'll limit myself to a brief rundown, so that the interested reader can
follow along.

His plane took off at 9:15 P.M., on September 25,
1966, at the airport of Kloten near Zürich. On
September 27 Erich von X. and his traveling companion Hans Neuner (whom Erich had asked to come
along as his photographer) were already visiting the
ruins of Cajarmarquilla near Lima, Peru. There he was
interested mainly in the man-sized holes in the ground,
209 of them in a straight line, which were supposedly
used as grain silos—an utterly absurd and absolutely il-
logical allegation.

September 28: Nazca, the airfield of the gods! As I
have already mentioned in my report dealing with my
trip into the remote past, this airfield did not yet exist at
the time of the Altairians. I never saw it then, though I
had known about it before my trip through photos and
reports. My conjectures do not coincide entirely with
those of Erich in that respect, but his, as well as my own
views, have the same origin. The drawings and the landing strips were undoubtedly intended for pilots who
arrived via the airways.

On September 29 Erich and Hans flew to Cuzco.
Cuzco and the fortress of Sacsayhuaman—that

was the key! That is where I had visited Professor Thomé in the past, and that is where Erich must find the traces of what had been new 23,000 years ago.

And he *did* find them!

Here is an account by Hans Neuner (although it has already been published elsewhere) which has been confirmed by Erich:

"While in Sacsayhuaman we visited only those areas which were not frequented by tourists. We continued to climb up another 600 meters, and there we found gigantic chunks of rock, smoothly polished, with sharp edges that could never have been the result of a natural process. There Erich discovered the first vitrifications of stone, and it seemed to me that he had been looking for them. He became greatly excited and wandered about for hours in the mountains in order to search for some evidence of former volcanic activity in this area. He arrived at the indisputable conclusion that there was no trace of volcanic activity in the vicinity. Even if there had been a volcanic eruption here, the lava masses would have flown downward only toward one side, never on *all* sides! The laws of gravity have functioned since time immemorial, even if they remained undiscovered as such until Newton came along. Vitrification of rock, however, is exclusively the result of tremendous generation of heat. How odd that so far nobody paid any attention to these stone vitrifications! So much has been written in scientific works about Sacsayhuaman, but no word was mentioned about the mysterious gigantic blocks of rock 600 meters above the fortress."

This is Hans Neuner's report. I believe any further comment would be superfluous.

On October 5 something happened in Tiahuanacu which has never been mentioned in any of Erich's books or in anything written about him. Even Hans Neuner was unable to tell about this event, for he wasn't with Erich constantly. He lost sight of him for several hours while he photographed the monoliths in the environs of Tiahuanacu. Hans was chatting with the natives who were working around that area, and was wondering all the while what business kept his friend Erich driving and wandering through these mountains so long.

Later on, I was the only person to learn what had taken place.

Here are the facts that have been concealed from everyone until now:

Erich von X.'s Reports, October 1966

"Today the decisive moment has come! Together with Hans Neuner I visited the fields of ruins at Tiahuanacu where we met a group of archaeologists and their helpers busy at work. We talked with them for a while. Upon hearing their ideas of how these ruins originated, what their history had been, I couldn't help but smile secretly to myself. These scientists actually believed that the primitive ancestors of the Incas had cut and polished the huge blocks of rock with their primitive stone hammers and stone chisels, laboring for many years to accomplish the degree of perfection in which we find these gigantic stones today. I held back from supplying them, right on the spot, the proof to the contrary. It would have been simplicity itself. The monoliths had been ground and polished so hard and precisely that even a steel chisel would have taken many days to cut a well-defined groove into the four-meter-high chunks of rock.

"And to top it all off: the water conduits!

"I almost burst out laughing when I saw how the workmen, who were following the instructions of the two archaeologists, had to fit several pieces of pipe into the reconstructed wall. The reconstruction was madness. They numbered the stones like a children's box of play bricks and then built a wall with them between two monoliths. Why don't any of these experts ever wonder about the meaning of the razor-edged, finger-wide grooves that run from the upper end of the monoliths down to the bottom in a straight line, as if drawn by a ruler? If ever they would pose this question, then it would never occur to them to join some smaller, square-hewn stones to a wall between the monoliths, which would only serve to cover up the grooves! These grooves were certainly made for some purpose—which was surely not to be senselessly hidden after so much painstaking labor!

"I did know the significance of the grooves. When the Altairian spaceship had constructed the first depot —before it had left the emigrants behind in such a dastardly fashion—the monoliths had served as anchoring points. They had bored a razor-sharp groove into each monolith, and then inserted from monolith to monolith, from above, a thin, artificial fiber panel into the prepared grooves. The upper, countersunk angles of the monolith had supported a flat roof—and the emergency depot was ready!

"And now the archaeologists were building—right in front of my eyes—a splendid specimen of a wall between the monoliths. I was itching to tell them what a grave mistake they were making here, that the stones they were fitting together dated from a much later period than the monoliths; also that the precisely worked pipe sections had not been water conduits. But what could I do? They would have inquired about my name, title, and academic standing—and after I'd admitted my amateur status they would have called me an ignoramus and a fool. It was senseless. I had to remain silent.

"First of all, there was the matter of getting rid of Hans, for I had not informed him of the story about Walter and the time machine, and therefore could not give him any plausible explanation why I expected to find a certain object at a definite place. So I instructed Hans to photograph the field of ruins from all sides and angles, and to shoot close-ups of certain individual items. Meanwhile, I—so I told him—would drive by car in the direction of Lake Titicaca, intending to return a few hours later. I brushed off my companion's objections, climbed into the red VW we had rented in La Paz, and drove off.

"The countryside appeared to have greatly changed during the past 23,000 years. It was incredibly difficult for me to find the way according to the few landmarks Walter had described. I relied therefore on my trusty Recta-compass, an excellent roadmap which I had purchased in La Paz, and also on the nearby mountains.

"The truncated cone of the mountaintop to the left in front of me—that must be it! No doubt, up there was the plateau where Walter and Thomé had waited to be polished off as a tasty dinner by the savages who had captured them. What a crazy thought: ten months ago I had talked with Walter in my Hotel Rosenhügel, and some 20,000 years ago he had hovered up here between life and death!

"What would have happened if the cannibals had eaten him up at that time? Would I have encountered Professor Thomé in Egypt in 1954, and would I not know Walter Ernsting today? Or had one thing nothing to do with the other?

"Now I was standing at the foot of the rock wall, scanning its surface closely with my field glasses, like a hunter stalking his prey. I noticed an opening in the wall which appeared to be man-made, and headed straight for it.

"The entrance to the cave was blocked by earth. There were hundreds of such caves in this area. Nobody was especially interested in them anymore. Many had been dug out by archaeologists, but they had never discovered anything more than a natural rift in the rock. Any hopes of discovering some Inca treasure in one of these caves had not materialized.

"There was no doubt that this was the entrance to the cave where Walter and Thomé had to leave the sphinx behind. I must try and get inside. I had only a few hours left.

"I carried no equipment with me, except for my Butane lighter, freshly filled, which burned with a large flame. The main problem was that some stones lay in front and inside the entrance, barring my way. Above the entrance rose the rock wall with the deep cleft which had endured many thousands of years—an unmistakable landmark! The rock pile had blocked the

actual entrance, but not the crevice immediately overhead. It was narrow, but I might perhaps manage to
squeeze through it.

"I put my hand into the cleft. I met with no resistance. With my fingers I removed the uppermost
stones until the opening grew large enough to accommodate my head and shoulders.

"But then, while I was halfway dangling in the
hole, my feet still unable to reach firm ground, I was
suddenly overcome by fear. Damn it, if I could only
get out of that hole again! Panting, I pulled myself up
with my arms, lay flat on my stomach on the ledge,
my upper body sticking out in the open, while the rest
of me was still hanging inside the cave. I rested for a
few moments to catch my breath, then climbed out
and stumbled the few meters across the rock-strewn
slope to my car.

"I needed a rope.

"I was triumphant when I actually discovered a
tow rope in the VW's trunk. I struggled up the slippery
rubble heap once more, anchored the rope around the
nearest tree, threw the other end into the hole, and
forced my body again through the narrow opening.
First I pushed my legs through, then my torso, groan-
ing with the effort.

"I slid down the wall inside, expecting to hit the
ground with a hard thump. I hardly fell a meter before
my feet touched ground. Light came through the cleft
in the wall, so I didn't need to use my Butane lighter
as I groped my way deeper into the cave.

"It was very narrow inside, and I had to walk
hunched over. Over the millennia, chunks of rock had
detached themselves from the ceiling and formed a
thick, impassable layer in the passageway. After I had
advanced some six meters, I had to use my lighter in
order to avoid breaking my neck.

"And then I reached the end of the corridor.

"Above Cuzco I had seen the interior of the pyramid and the barrier wall leading to the secret chamber
which harbored the time machine. I also had had a
good look at the 'keyhole' there. But I did not have

the key in my possession. Even if I were to find it now, there was no more time left in my travel schedule to return again to Cuzco.

"Anyhow, the time machine was not supposed to be used before the year 1968, as Thomé had informed me.

"The wall facing me at the end of the corridor was smooth but by no means polished. It looked like bare, roughly hewn rock. I realized this must be due to the traces time had left on it. I knew that on the other side of this wall lay one of the emergency depots constructed by the Altairians who perhaps had never made use of it.

"The 'keyhole' was located close to the floor of the corridor, just as Walter had described it.

"And, by Jove! Inside the 'keyhole' was stuck the sphinx, though it had been pushed in only part way!

"*My* sphinx! The one Thomé had found in Cuzco and had given me some eleven years ago! The *same* sphinx Walter had taken along on his journey into the past, still where he was forced to leave it behind some 23,000 years ago, right *here* on this spot!

"Where had the little stone figure *actually* been throughout all these thousands of years?

"Terribly excited, I pulled the figure out of its hiding place and examined it briefly. Below its right eye it indeed had the little nick someone had tried to repair—irrefutable proof that I was not holding an imitation in my hand. I weighed the pros and cons for a moment, then temptation won out. I decided to use this unique opportunity. I shoved the sphinx back into the keyhole, turned it in the manner I had been told by Walter, then pushed it all the way in.

"I felt the floor vibrate underneath my feet as the mechanism swung into action, and then the rock wall slid down into the ground. To tell the truth, I couldn't say which was trembling more, me or the wall! Without stepping across the threshold, I bent forward to lean inside the chamber, searching the area to the right of the barrier wall. I couldn't find a keyhole.

"How then was it possible to get out of this chamber again, once the barrier wall was shut?

"I did not dare cross the threshold. Nobody would ever find me up here!

"My Butane lighter provided only a very poor illumination. I increased the flame to give me more light. The gas would last no more than fifteen minutes. The light was bright enough now for me to look around the chamber.

"My caution had been justified.

"Inside the chamber, close to the threshold, lay four human skeletons, a few colorful rags still attached to the bones. They were ancient. As soon as the draft hit them, they simply fell apart. They must have been lying here for many thousands of years.

"I shuddered.

"Four persons had penetrated into the chamber, but failed to get out again.

"There must have been then a fifth person who had discovered and entered the cave, pulled the sphinx halfway out of its 'keyhole,' without investigating further the secret behind the wall. For unknown reasons he had left the figure sticking partially inside the hole, and then had left the cave again. It was only on account of this man's actions that I found today what lay now before my eyes.

"On the other side of the skeletons, along the walls, I noticed shelving made of some dull, shining, silver-gray material, stacked full with a variety of instruments which I could not make out too well. I discovered precisely made chests of silvery glittering metal which probably had served to store these sensitive instruments. The whole chamber was crammed full. All these objects would show our past in an entirely new light, if I should ever decide to reveal this secret.

"But the time was not yet ripe for this. The military, acting as usual like the busybodies they are, would use this treasure trove to forge newer and more powerful weapons.

"There was no time machine in the chamber.

"I was burning my fingers with my lighter, now too hot to hold any longer. I was afraid I might drop it and be left in total darkness, so I stepped outside again and pulled the sphinx from the hole in the wall. The barrier wall immediately began to rise up from the ground. I waited until the gate to the secret chamber was completely closed again and nothing but the bare rock could be seen. Then I beat a hasty retreat.

"A little while later I was standing outside again in broad daylight, the sphinx pressed under my arm and a hot lighter in my pocket.

"I drove slowly back to the field of ruins where Hans was waiting impatiently for me.

" 'Where have you been hiding all this time?'

"I held the sphinx out for him to see. 'Look and you will find,' I said, and strolled over to the archaeologists to have a talk with them. They admired the stone figure and asked where I had found it. 'Up in the mountains,' was my answer.

"The more serious of the two scientists regarded the statue. 'This confirms my theory,' he stated earnestly. 'The predecessors of the Incas worshipped the jaguar as their god. This is indubitably a jaguar.'

"Attempting to fight against such obvious wrong convictions was senseless.

"I had found what I had searched for.

"The next day we continued our journey."

*   *   *

This concludes Erich's report about finding the sphinx.

On October 11 he visited the ancient ruined Mayan city of Tikal in Guatemala, on October 14 he was in Mexico—and on October 21 at the rocket center in Houston, Texas. Here the past and the future encountered each other, and there was no difference between the two.

October 23: Cape Kennedy.

October 26: Huntsville, Alabama. Werner von Braun.

October 27: New York. Willy Ley.

October 28: Keene in New Hampshire. Professor Hapgood and the maps of Piri Reis.

October 31: Back again in Zürich!

And this is where he made the sad discovery: His debts had doubled. I visited Erich again in May 1967, but this time we did not meet in his hotel. Instead, we had arranged to go to a small resort town in the Vorarlberg, Austria, where nobody knew us and where we hoped to remain undisturbed.

The Arlberg mountain was still snowed in. Huge snowbanks rose to the right and to the left, and some peaks were still shrouded in clouds. For an instant I thought I was back in the Andes; then the mountain pass was behind me.

Erich was waiting for me. He had been smart enough to travel by train, and was sunning himself on the terrace of the small boardinghouse. This time his welcome was more cordial and more private than usual. There were none of the hectic everyday activities of the Rosenhügel, and Erich impressed me as being calmer and more confident. I had no idea of the difficulties he was involved in; he displayed no signs of trouble.

"I've finished the book," he announced after we had shaken hands. "I brought along the copy for you to read. The original manuscript is in Düsseldorf, in the hands of a publisher with a lot of enterprising spirit. He won't regret it."

"Have you mentioned anything about Thomé?"

He shook his head so energetically that I decided against asking any further questions.

"Do you think I'm tired of living, Walter? What I've written so far will do amply for the initial shock. You can bet your life it's going to be a shock. I want to shake and awaken the man in the street, incite him to think—cause a great deal of alarm in certain circles. My book is breaking hundreds of taboos which kept constricting us, so far preventing us from a logical approach to many ideas. I'm quite prepared to encounter a bitter fight, a fight against the conservative science of archaeology, its founders and its followers. And especially for a fight against those envious people who will accuse me of ignorance and an overdeveloped imagination."

"The world has always had its heretics," I tried to comfort him. "And later on it turned out they were right."

Erich raised his glass. "Yes, later—after they were dead."

The owner of the boardinghouse, a genial, older lady, showed me to my room. I changed clothes and returned to the terrace where Erich was still sitting. I noticed gratefully that a second glass of cool, refreshing beer was waiting for me on the table.

"I have to get back tomorrow," said Erich, looking up to the mountain peaks. The cloudless sky had turned a deep blue. "Money, you know."

"Is it that bad?"

"Yes and no. We had bad luck with our winter season. More expenses than we took in. Add to that some new investments that could no longer be put off. The hotel is doing better, though, all the time. I'll be out of the red in three years. Well, none of my creditors is giving me a hard time but, still, it's not a very pleasant feeling to be in debt. Let's hope the guys in Düsseldorf will hurry up with my book! How long does something like that usually take?"

He had actually not the faintest idea how much work is necessary to bring out a book. It might be written fairly fast under certain circumstances, but then it lands in the publishing mill. The manuscript must be edited, often changed, then printed and proofread, maybe edited once more. That means many pages may have to be printed a second time. Then, thinking up a proper title and the cover illustration. The publisher makes his selection from the rough drafts, then passes them on to the proper places to be executed to his satisfaction.

Weeks and months go by.

It may take a year.

"Three to four months," I said.

"That long? For heaven's sake, I don't have that much time!"

"Do you know the publisher? Can't he give you an advance? After all, he signed the contract for the book."

"More debts?" Erich shook his head in horror. "I have it up to here with debts." He emptied his glass. "Come along, let's go for a walk. I must get a good whiff of the mountain air to clear my head of the cobwebs. There is a footpath just behind the house."

For more than two hours we wandered through the woods, the trees covered with new green leaves, past meadows where the first cows were grazing in the fresh, young grass. It was still cold during the nights, and the cattle were driven back to the cowsheds every afternoon. Our conversation touched mainly on general topics and some private matters; not until we were sitting on a sunny bench high above the valley did I ponder aloud. "If it were possible to conduct a proper search down there in the valley, a lot of evidence would be uncovered that human beings were living here also, before they were supposed to do so according to the laws set down by our scientists. I am quite certain— and in this point I am in agreement with Jacques Bergier—that a technologically advanced civilization must have existed between Neanderthal man and Cro-Magnon man. This civilization ended abruptly and left no visible traces behind." I looked at my companion. "You've read enough science fiction novels—what does it look like, in your opinion? Is there a lot left?"

He contemplated the valley below, which had somehow kept a primeval appearance; followed the meandering course the brook had cut into the rocks; admired the will to live of those trees that had established a foothold on bare outcroppings, whose roots managed to extract sustenance from the hostile environment. The appearance of the landscape had probably not changed for 5,000 years except for the houses dotting the valley floor.

"No, there isn't much that remains. It depends on

the radiation following such a catastrophe. The explosion will destroy everything on the surface of the land. And even more so the fire storm afterward. But it's quite possible that plants and insects in particular survive the holocaust and manage to recover from it. The flora and the fauna erase the traces the cataclysm left behind—in the course of centuries. There might also be some human beings who survive the catastrophe. They'll adjust to the new living conditions in their altered environment. They have to start from scratch again—that's for sure. Maybe they find some remainders of our civilization, somewhere in underground bunkers or narrow side valleys that were miraculously spared. But two to three generations later, the world as we know it today has halfway become legend already. Imagine, Walter: Two or three generations will suffice to let the memory fade away."

I silently nodded my head to express my agreement. After a while Erich added: "Some eight hundred generations have lived on Earth since the Altairians landed here twenty-three thousand years ago. What else needs to be said?"

"And sixty generations ago Jesus Christ was born," I said.

"Correct! And do we really know what *actually* happened at that time?"

He gave me a peculiar look, then suggested: "You and I—we can make a good guess, I'm sure. Everything fits too well into the scheme of things that always precede the founding of a new religion. Christianity is nothing but an imitation! Don't get upset; I know that a Christian education is a great advantage for children."

"Yes, indeed—" I couldn't help letting the words out of my mouth—"for children!"

He fell silent.

That was the end of the discussion. A little while later, we strolled back to our boardinghouse. Since we were the only guests, we shared supper with the family.

Later that evening, we sat in the deserted dining room where we could converse leisurely. The absence of crowds and their noise felt very soothing to our nerves. Now and again the waitress appeared to inquire after our wishes. We drank wine Erich had selected.

"If I have the money, I'll go on another trip in the fall of 1968," Erich suddenly said, startling me. "This time it won't be just to Europe and America but also to Africa, Asia, and India. Especially India! Many interesting things are to be seen there. You have to observe them with spaced-out eyes, and I certainly qualify in this respect. Some people will soon be inclined to think I've lost the ability to see things the way ordinary people do."

"Why don't you first wait and see if your book is a success?" I tried to dampen his excessive optimism. In the case of books, especially where my own are concerned, I am a pessimist on principle. I'm always happy to be wrong. "A book's success doesn't always depend on whether it's good or bad. Either kind may make it."

"I *know* my book will make it!" he replied.

It was late when we finally decided to call it a day.

The next morning I accompanied him to the railroad station. "When will we meet again?"

He leaned out of the open window of his train compartment so as not to have to shout. "If I have to go back to Düsseldorf, I'll stop over to see you in Salzburg."

The train started moving.

"Lots of luck, Erich!" I called out, and waved good-bye. "For South America!"

I stayed for another day in the quiet boardinghouse in Vorarlberg before I started out on my return trip to Salzburg. When I arrived back home, a new outline of my science fiction series was waiting for my immediate attention.

While I was writing about the world of the year 3000 A.D., I gradually returned to the world of reality. The future was less utopian and fantastic than the far distant past.

Somewhere on our globe, the extraterrestrials were biding their time. I knew it. I could sense it!

They were keeping us under surveillance.

* * *

Over the next three months I saw Erich three more times.

As promised, he visited me in Salzburg. I picked him up from the railroad station, and that evening we sat for a long time in my studio. None of my acquaintances had any idea that my guest was a man destined to become famous, infamous, and notorious all at once. As for me, Erich was simply a friend whose opinions and views I shared. This bond of friendship would grow stronger still the following year.

"My book is as good as completed," he announced, radiant with joy. "One more step, and then it will go into production. Then the shekels will roll in, and I can make good my promises."

"Let's hope so." I warned him to remain cautious. "If not, you'll get into a lot of trouble."

"But if I declare bankruptcy with my hotel, then my creditors will be the ones to get into trouble. So they'd better be patient."

Sometimes I couldn't quite understand my friend and his way of reasoning. Evidently, he had even less know-how regarding business matters than I—and I'm definitely no expert. But Erich was too good a person. That may sound strange, but it is the truth. If he had been a real businessman, he would have filed for the official bankruptcy proceedings, and no one would ever have been able to touch a hair of his head. Unfortunately for Erich von X., he was not.

He was a man of honest principles, and they led him to his doom.

"When will *Chariots of the Gods?* appear?"

"Next February—about three months."

"Won't you run into any difficulties with your debts? Will your creditors wait that long?"

"I think so. They all know that I don't have

the money yet to pay them off. I'm sure they are just as anxious for my book to come out as I am."

"Then they'll certainly buy it," I laughed confidently.

That entire evening we discussed publishers, fees, and royalties, topics I have more experience with than my friend Erich. In the meantime I had obtained a copy of his manuscript. I read it repeatedly, admiring Erich's skill in mixing facts and speculations so that it would never have occurred to the initiated that he was one of them. I was particularly relieved that he never once mentioned my name in his book. I must admit, my pride suffered. Without my journey into the past he could never have written his work with such strength of conviction and persuasion, which undoubtedly greatly contributed to its later success. On the other hand, it was better for me if my name was kept in the dark.

When we met next time, several months later in Davos, the name of Erich von X. was already on the best-seller list of the German news magazine, *Der Spiegel*. His hotel was surviving, but with such minimal profits that it was still out of the question to repay his large debts.

But his book was doing very well indeed. The publishers brought out one edition after another. Erich used the royalties to settle his financial obligations one after the other. However, many creditors still remained. Erich had living expenses, and in addition had to incur many new costs, for now he had become suddenly a man very much in demand. TV interviews and lecture tours forced him again and again to leave his Rosehill Hotel and spend the night in costly hotel rooms. But all these promotional activities helped cause a phenomenal rise in sales of his *Chariots of the Gods*.

He had not changed at all. I got my old room in the Rosehill, although the hotel was completely sold out. Before I had a chance to change clothes, he appeared in my door, merrily waving a half-filled bottle of bourbon. "This one we can enjoy with a good conscience, Walter—it's paid for!"

I'm fond of ironic jokes. After we had drunk a first toast to his book, I handed him a copy I had bought myself and asked him for his autograph. Rarely have I seen somebody grin so triumphantly as when he borrowed my pen to write a dedication of a few simple words on the title page.

"That's just to serve as camouflage," he said, and pushed the book across the tabletop toward me. "I don't want to get you involved in my own troubles."

"What reactions did you get? I don't mean the literary critics."

"You mean from the scientific world?" He impatiently waved his right hand. "Just as expected. They declare I'm a charlatan, a fraud, a speculator—any derogatory label they can pin on me. After all, I have studied neither archaeology nor theology. Furthermore, I'm considered to be arrogant. I've foreseen all these reactions; They don't surprise me in the least."

"No, Erich, I didn't mean these either. But if the Altairian control station still does exist, its influence would now gradually become noticeable. They can't remain inactive while they observe the sudden collapse of a world view which took thousands of years to grow."

"I don't see why not. Maybe they even find it desirable! Those Altairians, the illegal emigrants to our planet Earth who managed to survive the holocaust more than twenty-three thousand years ago, became dispersed to all parts of this world, as Thomé correctly stated. They were far superior in every respect to the primitive native population of that era, even if the refugees tried to hide this fact as much as possible. For sheer survival, they were *forced* to deploy their technical knowledge. This is how the legends came about. The alien survivors became the gods of remote antiquity, the heroes of our legends, the fairy-tale figures alive to this day in the folklore of all nations. This phenomenon cannot be undone. I see no reason why the control base should intervene. In any case, I'm not supplying any proofs. My adversaries believe I'm making a fool of myself—and that this will finish me off."

"Our friend Kofol is convinced the extraterrestrials ought to be your main opponents. Do you agree?"

"Quite the contrary! Today mankind is standing at the threshold of outer space. I believe the extraterrestrials are definitely interested in slowly and cautiously preparing us to realize our true identity."

"If, despite all this, they should still turn out to be your enemies? Andreas Kofol has come to the conclusion that they would resort to using human tactics. There are many ways they could go about it. And there are lots of shady lawyers or power-hungry district attorneys they might manipulate as their puppets."

"I have done nothing wrong."

"Most people who are brought to trial share that opinion. Don't get me wrong: I have no intention of aggravating you—only to warn you to be on your guard. Be sure you never do anything that is liable to be misinterpreted."

"If you are referring to my debts—I've got rid of a great many already. And I'll take care of the rest. Money just keeps coming in from my book."

"Great. Maybe you'll clear up all your debts by next fall."

His face did not seem too confident.

"But I have to save money for my next trip, too. It's hard to put money aside when you have to pay off some debts. I want my next book to be a huge success. I've had too little time so far to have a thorough look at all that's necessary to keep my data straight. Besides, I intend to get inside the crystal labyrinth this time around—especially since I've got the 'key' back."

"Into the crystal labyrinth for your second book?" I was so flabbergasted that I was speechless for a moment. Then I found my tongue again. "Man alive, you've just written one best seller! Why don't you wait till everything is straightened out here?"

Erich's answer to that was, simply: "The time is ripe, Walter."

I knew how right he was.

While we attacked our second bottle of wine, he told me the latest news:

"Last week I was in Moscow, where I spoke with Shklowskii and Alexander Kassanzew and the geophysicist Solotov. I was eager to clear up the mystery of that strange occurrence in the Siberian taiga on June 30, 1908. You are familiar with that, I'm sure. Till this very day, radioactivity is stronger there than anywhere else in the world. There is no doubt that an atomic explosion took place there more than sixty years ago. Was it a spaceship with nuclear drive that crashed down to Earth? A warning of the extraterrestrial control base? We don't know, but the Russian scientists are convinced that this was not a mere meteor. It was an artificial explosion. I taped interviews with these men, and listened to them later that day in my hotel room. They were first-class recordings. When I arrived in Davos, the tapes has been erased. Nothing left of the interview—not a sound! Now I'm asking you, Walter: Who erased these tapes? The Russians? And why?" He shook his head pensively.

For the rest of that evening, Erich spoke a great deal about his planned trip. He was firmly resolved to use the time machine this time. He wanted to obtain first-hand confirmation that his conjectures were correct, and to add new insights and data to what he had surmised all these many years.

Even when I pointed out to him that Thomé's calculations about the various dates might not be entirely exact, he was not willing to change his plans in any way.

We arranged for a final meeting a week before his scheduled departure. On Sunday, the 8th of September 1968, I was sitting together with Andreas Kofol and my secretary, Ann, in the hotel Maria Theresa in Innsbruck. We were waiting for our friend Erich, who was notorious for sleeping late, to appear.

It was a long day, filled with discussions and long walks through the magnificent old Austrian city. A clear blue sky arched over the glittering roofs and the surrounding mountains, a summery sky which let us forget that fall was near. Erich was not bothered by the thought of the approaching cold season; he was soon to fly off to a warmer climate. It was quite obvious for all to see that he was feverishly awaiting the day when he could finally leave.

Later that evening we gathered in the Jägerstube, one of the hotel's restaurants. Erich had invited all of us to have dinner with him. His traveling companion, Hans Neuner, with his fiancée Brigitte Moser, had joined our party. We made a very cheerful group—if only I had not been beset by a feeling of apprehension. It came from deep inside my subconscious mind, could not be analyzed, and escaped any tangible comprehension. Maybe it was caused by a conversation we had had that afternoon. Kofol had again urgently warned our friend Erich to be very cautious on his journey and, as he phrased it—a bit exaggeratedly in my opinion—always to be on the lookout for insidious attacks.

Now, as we were dawdling over our after-dinner drinks, Erich resumed the discussion of a familiar topic.

"My dear doctor, I don't wish to be insulting. But do you seriously believe that we are under the surveillance of extraterrestrials?"

I was probably just as dumbfounded by this question as my poor friend Kofol, who simply gaped at Erich. I was well aware that my physician friend from Salzburg believed in mankind being controlled by intelligences from outer space—long before he had made Erich's and my acquaintances. In his opinion there was an abundance of proof for this view. My own time travel into the past confirmed his assertion, at least as far as the distant past was concerned. It was, however, entirely possible that the Galactic Federation had long since abandoned Earth as a guinea pig for its cosmogenetic experimentations, and that the control station was therefore no longer in existence.

Yet there was no proof either way.

"But Mr. von X.——!" Andreas Kofol quite audibly was gasping for air. *"You, of all people,* would doubt that? Sure, if I told this to just anybody I would expect him to think I'm crazy. I would feel the same in his place. But you know as well as I do that the present is always a product of the past. And that the Altairians conducted genetic experiments in the past with the rather primitive human race of that time; that is a proven fact for us, the initiated. This was not done without reason or just for the sake of the experiment itself. They wanted to wait for the result and eventually derive some advantage from it." At this point Kofol even managed to grin broadly. "Who knows, maybe the Galactic Federation awards a special bonus for those races who win new members for their league of cosmic nations this way." I couldn't help shaking my head in amazement.

"You should also take up writing science fiction, too," I suggested.

He growled at me, displeased, and kept trying to accommodate his stout body to the limited confines of his armchair, which was obviously too small for his bulk.

Erich managed a compassionate smile. "Bravo, Doctor! Your strong reaction proves to me that you really believe in what you are saying. That's all I wanted to know for the time being. Don't worry about me. If our conjectures on the existence of the control base are correct, then all the other related facts will prove out. The extraterrestrials won't cause me any difficulties, at least none that might endanger my life. Everything else I can take care of."

"Will you write to us?"

"I always try—if time permits."

It was late when we took leave of each other. Early next day, Erich had to start out on a lecture tour which eventually brought him back again to Davos. Less than a week later he was boarding Swissair flight 100 to New York.

Andreas Kofol, Ann, and I drove back to Salzburg on Monday morning. It was a stroke of luck that I had asked my secretary to come along to Innsbruck. She was busy taking notes, which turned out to be of tremendous value to me later on. We returned to our routine.

From that day on there was nothing for me to do but wait.

To wait to learn whether Andreas Kofol's fears were justified, and whether something untoward would happen to Erich on this trip.

Little did we know that the unknown foe had already secretly set things in motion to deal Erich a crippling blow.

Man's worst enemy is his own kind.

seven

My time was fully occupied with my work writing a popular science fiction series. Our writing team had meanwhile decided—after first obtaining the publisher's consent—to utilize the by now widely discussed "von X. theme" as a science fiction topic within the framework of the well-established series of interconnected novels. That necessitated a great deal of research and study of the pertinent and specialized technical literature. It left no time for private matters.

There was no news from Erich. It seemed as if the Earth had swallowed him up.

The month of September went by.

I received his first letter on October 3. It carried the letterhead of the Hotel Europe in San Jose, Costa Rica.

He wrote:

> Everything is going fine. I made some amazing discoveries here that should also be of interest to you. My journey proceeds according to plan. I found some fabulous things in the Library of Congress in the USA,

about Piri Reis. I photographed some documents with my Minox 36. Unfortunately, the film can't be developed until I get home. For your information I'm including copies of the Piri Reis map. When you're done with it, please forward it to my home address. I had long talks with the officials appointed to deal with the Piri Reis map. We are all agreed on one point: There is something suspicious about our past.

So far we haven't sighted any UFOs. "Big Brother" is playing hide-and-seek. Remember me to Dr. Kofol.

Cordially,
Erich

The allusion to the control station was unmistakable.

A few additional short notes followed, and on October 9 Erich arrived in Lima, Peru, from where he planned to start out on a one-week trip to Nazca.

What happened during the interval between the 9th and 17th of October 1968 I learned only in a roundabout way. According to the official version, he spent that time in and near Nazca to study the "landing grounds and airfield of the gods."

Toward the end of October he visited Easter Island. He arrived in Paris on November 5, immediately flying off from there to India.

Both Dr. Kofol and I received some mail from India. While Erich mentioned only his "blessed cosmic eyes" in his brief missile to me, he wrote to Kofol, probably heedful of his warning:

"I'm encountering now totally unexpected difficulties. I hope I'll make it through the 15th round. See you in Innsbruck or Salzburg end of this month. E.v.D."

On November 15 Erich flew from India to Beirut to see the mysterious terraces of Baalbek, which have posed so many riddles to scientists.

On November 19, 1968, when Erich's plane made a brief landing in Vienna, he was arrested by Interpol.

What ensued has become common knowledge through the press, partially slanted and nonobjective in their reports. These exerted a negative influence on a lot of people, who in turn took a stand against von X. and his theories. Only a minority attempted to find out what was behind this incident.

To this minority belonged two journalists from Vienna and Salzburg—well known to me personally —who did their utmost to direct the public's attention to the improper, even hair-raising procedure of certain authorities. It's most likely thanks to the two journalists' articles, that Erich von X. was not immediately condemned lock, stock, and barrel. But critical voices were coming from all circles of the population.

There is no need to mention what Dr. Kofol and I thought of the whole affair. Only one thing mattered to me now. How could I establish contact with the accused in custody to reassure him that we knew what the score really was . . . ?

It was a tedious path which led by way of Hans Neuner, his fiancée Brigitte, and eventually to Erich's wife, Elisabeth. We managed to get the better of the pretrial judge in Davos, and when Elisabeth obtained a permit to visit her husband in the Viennese prison, I breathed a sigh of relief.

But all these efforts took many weeks, and we were well into the new year, 1969, by then.

On February 12, 1969, the gates of the Sennhof prison in Chur, Switzerland, closed behind Erich. Austria had finally extradited the prominent prisoner, who had become a nuisance, to his homeland where the prosecution had originated. Erich's publisher in Düsseldorf kept printing and selling one edition after another of *Chariots of the Gods?*, and informed me that the author had nearly finished the manuscript for his second book, although only in first-draft form and so far without the proper documentation.

Now he was held there in custody, awaiting his trial. While Erich had to endure the red tape of bureaucracy and the slowly-grinding mills of justice, he doggedly kept writing his book.

In less than six weeks he finished it, without having access to his notes or other documentation. His publisher informed me it was an incredible achievement. "It's inconceivable how he could write a book at all under the circumstances!"

The book, *Gods from Outer Space,* was scheduled to appear in September 1968.

And it was actually brought out while its author was sitting in prison, awaiting his trial. Its first edition of 100,000 copies was immediately sold out. In my estimation Erich must by then have been out of debt. He had been able to pay off all he owed while held in custody.

When I read the book my last doubts were dispelled. I received the final, absolute confirmation of what I had guessed already, through an innocuous sounding postcard from Erich's brother:

Dear Mr. Ernsting,
      Yesterday I visited Erich. He is fine and thanks you for your help. He instructed me very urgently to convey to you best regards from a Professor Thomé whom he met in the middle of last October in Cuzco.
                         Cordially,
                            Yours, ..."

So Erich had been in the past!

He had returned safe and sound. All the unpleasant circumstances surrounding his arrest, the uncertainty and injustice, had not been able to hold him back from writing down his experiences while their memory was still fresh in his mind.

As fascinating a book as *Gods from Outer Space* might be, I was feverishly looking forward to a report exclusively for me. Someday Erich would find a way of smuggling it out of prison. Then I'd finally learn

what had happened a year and a half after my visit
with the Altairians.

But I had to wait a long time for that day.

* * *

During the Second World War, I spent three years
in Norway. Ever since, for twenty-five years, it had
been my greatest desire to see again this magnificent
country and its hospitable people. The opportunity
arose in 1970 when one of my old school friends had
the glorious idea of undertaking a journey to the far
north. He planned it as a camping trip, leaving his
family behind. But he remembered just in time that I
had traveled in an armored truck all over Lappland
for three years with my commanding officer and therefore invited me to accompany him as a kind of travel
guide.

We met in June to discuss the details of our
journey. I was supposed to drive my own car to Hamburg at the beginning of July, leaving it there in my
friend's garage. He owned a fully-equipped VW bus
which would serve as a camper during our expedition
to the north.

In the meantime—to be exact, on February 13,
1970—Erich had been sentenced to three and a half
years in prison.

His two books were doing very well, maybe even
better than before he started his prison term. His debts
had all been paid off a long time since. There was
nothing I could do to help him now, so I accepted
Helmut's offer.

I arrived in Hamburg on July 3.

It was not just the opportunity to see Norway
again that had induced me to accept Helmut's invitation. Deep in my subconscious there slumbered a vague
memory. During the war, in Lappland, I had had an
experience I had never completely understood. Not until this day, when I was so close to a reunion with the
grand solitude of this land, when the war lay so far
behind me, did the memory of this incident slowly
return: Like a diver seeking treasure deep below the

ocean's surface, oppressed by the darkness of the depths, then overcome with relief when he can finally rise up again. While he is swimming toward the sun, everything around him turns brighter and brighter until he finally breaks through the surface into the light of day—or into the reemerged memory.

Now it was Helmut's turn to drive the car while I rested in the back seat, trying to submerge myself in the twenty-eight-year-old past.

* * *

My unit—Air Force Intelligence—was stationed in Banak, on a peninsula at the end of Porsanger Fjord. The fjord reached more than 100 kilometers inland, just south of the North Cape. There were no large buildings here, just the huts of the native fishermen and the barracks built by the German army. The airport was the northernmost in the world. From here the squadrons of the fifth air-fleet bombed the convoys attempting to sail around the North Cape in order to reach the Russian port of Murmansk.

I had been there for two years, with short sojourns in Oslo, Bergen, Tromsö, and Narvik. Every day I thanked my good fate that I was there, and not somewhere else. I could not imagine what it would be like to have to be at the front. Even all the charms of life in Paris would not have tempted me. I loved the primeval landscape around Lakselv and the nearby swamps of Skoganvarre. And to top it off, I had been assigned an enviable job as driver of the commanding officer.

The old Opel-Kapitän was definitely not the most suitable vehicle for the roads in Lappland, but so far it had never left me stranded. About two or three times a month, my major visited the various detachments which often were separated by a hundred kilometers. I became thoroughly acquainted with the coast roads as well as the areas farther inland.

While the midsummer night sun was shining, from June to August, it was often unbearably hot during the day, although the zone of eternal snow here was hardly

300 meters above sea level. The nearby swamps were swarming with clouds of gnats and mosquitoes, hovering above the numerous murky puddles of water. Anyone wanting to take a sunbath had better wait till night, when the insect pests were not biting so fiercely.

From time to time, English prisoners of war arrived. They were accommodated separately from us, in their own unfenced barracks. Nobody was afraid our prisoners might attempt to escape. There was no village or even settlement anywhere near us. And besides, the Englishmen were only too glad not to have to go on any more flight missions. They were mostly the survivors of shot-down aircraft. They led a wonderful life. In the daytime they were either lying inside or on the roof of their barracks sunning themselves. At night they were permitted to stay out until 10 o'clock. Since there was only one place in all of Banak where it was worthwhile spending one's free time, you'd always find them in the bar of our P.X. Although there were strict orders for the Norwegian barman not to sell any alcoholic beverages to our prisoners—a rule he strictly adhered to—nobody was surprised that our Tommies would return nightly to their barracks in a rather tipsy condition. For the rules did not forbid us to treat them to a few drinks of aquavit.

One day Charlie, the commander's servant, came to see me as I was just about to polish my Opel all over with diesel oil so that it would look shiny and ready for the road, an old trick frequently used by privates—which worked, however, only for a very short period of time. It took very few kilometers on a dusty road—and there were no other roads in Lappland—before the car would acquire a gray camouflaging color which made it almost invisible from the air. If ever my major had objected to this "anointing" of his car, it would have been easy for me to convince him of the life-saving aspect of this method.

"Something's cooking," Charlie announced. He knew all the latrine rumors a good two days ahead of time. "We're getting a JU-52, extra for our company."

Everybody knew what a JU-52 was: a three-engine

airplane, very safe but slow. It served to transport people and supplies.

I put my oil rag on the fender.

"What do they want to do with it here? Fly us out on leave?"

"Oh, baloney! The second and third platoon have been stringing up telegraph lines at the Tanaelv, across country. There aren't any roads there, so how are they supposed to get the material they need? With the good old JU, naturally. Get it?"

That seemed to make sense to some degree.

"Air-drop? Insulators, rolls of wire, and all the rest?"

"Yes, with parachutes, of course. The first tryout runs begin tomorrow on the landing strip. Want to come along? The guy from K.P. has volunteered already."

"Well, if the old man doesn't want to go for a drive tomorrow . . ."

"I'd know if he would. No, he's too busy right here."

I'd been on many flights, but never yet with a JU. Since it had the reputation of being especially safe, I did not hesitate to accept. While Charlie strolled off, I hurriedly rubbed on the remaining diesel oil and drove the car into the garage, an open shed next to the barracks.

The following day we were standing beside the machine. A few soldiers from the technical corps had packed three rolls of copper wire in wooden crates and attached them to a folded-up freight parachute. The insulators had been imbedded in wood shavings to make sure they would not break upon impact on the ground. The technicians wanted to ascertain if these precautionary measures were sufficient, and whether the wooden boxes could be dropped on target in this very difficult terrain.

A little later we took off, heading south. Way below I could make out the winding, narrow road to Karasjok, the capital city of the Lapplanders. Then our plane veered to the east until we flew above the Tana River, which formed the border between Norway and Finland.

This river had its source south of Karasjok, and was navigable for the narrow, small boats of the Lapplanders as long as they knew how to guide their crafts through the many rapids. These occurred every two or three kilometers—easily seen from the air—and if this obstacle had not existed I could have made a good suggestion how to transport rolls of wire and insulators to the construction crews.

The JU-52 descended. It was almost as if the plane's wide wingtips were brushing against the mountain slopes, but then I reassured myself that our pilot certainly knew what to expect from this old kite.

Charlie studied the map. "We've almost reached the little tributary with the small lake. There's a sand-bar—that's where we're supposed to drop the stuff. Hope we'll hit the sand-bar, at least."

The pilot gave us the final instructions, then made for the target after we had discovered our buddies waving to us from the sand bank. The first crate with the insulators left the machine through an opening in the plane's side where a door should have been. The parachute opened, and the box landed promptly in the water twenty meters off the sand bank, from where it could be easily retrieved.

The other crates and the bales of wire followed. Two of the missiles were right on target, and we congratulated each other on a successfully accomplished mission. The pilot turned around and set course for our home base.

Above Skoganvarre he veered toward the west in order to shorten the flight distance. I was sitting in the gunner's cockpit, but our JU carried neither a gunner nor an MG-15 aboard. That had the best view, and I thoroughly enjoyed it.

The Tana River flowed through a regular Scandinavian jungle. To the right and to the left stretched impassable bush and uninhabited swamps. The terrain was dotted with low hills. There were no mountains except for a round-topped peak toward the east, thirty kilometers away on Finnish soil. I would certainly not have noticed the mountain had it not been for a very strange phenomenon. It was late afternoon, and the sun was low in the western sky. The sun would not set entirely but would reach its nadir toward midnight; then it would rise again. At this moment the sun's rays fell exactly on the round summit, which rose above the haze of the extensive swamps and forest lands like a deserted island.

Suddenly the mountain's peak flashed up as if it were made of pure gold.

Before I had a chance to recover from my surprise or tell about my amazing discovery, the round-topped mountain reassumed the same appearance as before—a snow-covered peak rising some three or four hundred meters above the plain.

Yet it seemed a rather curiously rounded off summit, almost like the upper part of a hemisphere sunk into the rock.

A while later we landed safe and sound in Banak.

I had not spoken to anyone about my strange discovery; besides, the mountain had rapidly vanished from view in the haze that hovered over the swampland. At first I was inclined to think that this might be a secret hideout of the Norwegian resistance movement, which had relaxed its camouflage for a few moments when our plane was changing course. By sheer accident I had become acquainted with a few of these patriots, and it was out of the question that I'd ever betray them.

However, even if this had not been a guerrilla base, it would have been wrong to tell the others about my observation. Supposing we had flown back and reconnoitered the area, using up precious fuel. Nothing much would have come of it. I was certain we'd perceived nothing more than the round, snow-covered mountaintop.

Yet I felt convinced that my senses had not deceived me. Even if I assumed that the sun's rays coming from the west had hit the snow mountain from a certain angle, thus causing a corresponding reflection, such a precise golden coloration would never have resulted. And a simple mirage was even less likely to have been the cause of this phenomenon.

I could have found a natural explanation for any normal, momentary flash illuminating the rounded peak, but not so for a golden sheen lasting several seconds. It could only be something artificial.

The next day we learned that our bales of wire had safely landed. They had hardly been bent by the impact on reaching the ground. They were immediately put to use. Not so the insulators. More than half had not withstood the impact, even though our men had taken special care to pack them properly.

The result was that we continued to airlift and drop the bales of wire, while the sensitive insulators had to be transported in some other manner to the construction crews. Since it was out of the question to do this overland, only the waterways remained. As if I had had a hunch . . . !

Charlie—who else?—told me the news: "By truck to Karasjok, then reload into a rubber-dinghy. A two-man crew, provisions for a week on board, a rifle and ammunition—and of course a lot of good advice for the men on the road. It's a change of pace, wouldn't you say?"

"And who's supposed to go on that mission?"

"Who would you guess? The pencil pushers, the KP's and the drivers that are bumming around here. You are part of that crew. The old man has assigned you to the third team, together with Kurt. I wish you lots of luck with that guy."

I had nothing against Kurt from the orderly room. I had also nothing against this adventurous-sounding enterprise, for I already knew the area from the air. And we hardly had to fear any encounters with the enemy.

"What are those rubber dinghies like?"

"I haven't the faintest idea. We'll borrow them from the engineers. The boats have no motors, just paddles. They'll take some weight off fatso Kurt."

The first two boats started out three days later from Karasjok. To make quite sure they would not vanish somewhere in the jungle, or get stuck in one of the many river rapids, a Fiesler Storch flew a daily patrol mission along the river, marking the location of the dinghies that became separated and tried, individually, to reach their destination. One of the boats took four days, the other five, to get to the construction crew. The insulators were undamaged, although they had twice landed in the water underneath the tipped-over boats. The main thing was that the telegraph line could continue to be built.

Kurt and I were sent out alone. The Storch returned to Hammerfest with orders to see that the Norwegian fishermen did not maintain too close a contact with the Englishmen. Thus we were all on our own, a fact for which I was most grateful. My commander had no idea what I had in mind.

I was planning a detour to my golden mountain!

Everything went smoothly. The first stretch out of Karasjok was relatively free of danger. The Lapplanders were lolling about along the shore, grinning broadly as we floated past them. They called out to us, but we did not understand, of course. Most likely they were cursing us and wishing that we'd break our necks, for they were not too kindly disposed toward their German guests.

The sole reason we managed to pass through the first rapids, about two kilometers from the village, without being hurled against the sharp rocks, was due to Kurt's heroic sacrifice. He jumped into the water and, standing up to his hips in the icy, swirling floods, he steered the four-meter-long rubber boat. His missing weight in the dinghy had a beneficial effect; we drew that much less water and therefore did not get stuck on every little sand bank we passed. Shortly before we reached calmer waters, Kurt climbed back aboard.

"It's damned cold!" he stated, and shivered all

over. "Let's get ashore and build a fire. I don't want to catch pneumonia."

"Oh, just get rid of your wet clothes. The sun is warm enough, and there's nobody around here to see you. No houses, no people for miles around."

We were already deep inside the northern primeval forest. The stunted trees and bushes grew in such profusion, and so close together, that it was almost impossible to see farther than ten meters inland.

After half an hour had passed, Kurt put his dried clothes on again. And when we heard the distant roar of the next rapids we were approaching, he informed me firmly that it was now my turn to take a dip. I tried to convince him that we could manage without it, and in case we failed it was solely because of his excessive weight.

We were sailing downstream with ever-increasing speed, using our paddles only to steer the boat—and not always coordinating our handling of the clumsy oars to the best advantage. After rounding a curve in the river, we perceived the first rocky reefs, which formed a regular barrier in the middle of the stream. But we had meanwhile become such experts that we floated past them without so much as touching any of the rocks jutting out of the water. We made an elegant landing on the sand bank, formed by alluvial deposits beyond the reef.

There the water was just ankle-deep, but we both had to jump overboard into the water to get our obstinate dinghy afloat once more. After several encouraging shouts of "Heave-ho," the current nearly tore the rubber boat from our hands. We clambered aboard, happy in the knowledge that we had successfully overcome another obstacle in our path.

We stayed overnight with a fisherman, twenty kilometers below Karasjok. The whole family assembled on the river bank and looked with astonished eyes at the strange contraption that showed so little resemblance to the narrow, long, and easily maneuverable boats of the Lapplanders. The children were dead-set on trying it out, and Kurt was glad to oblige.

While he was paddling the youngsters in the still backwaters of an old river arm, I was doing my best to fraternize with the natives.

For supper they served bread, butter, eggs, and fish. We contributed a can of roast beef and some sausage. Later that evening, satiated and contented, we crawled under our blankets in the hayloft, where we were bedded down for the night. We slept soundly and without dreams till the next morning.

That day we covered a distance of some thirty kilometers, ran aground altogether four times, capsized our craft once, although fortunately in shallow waters so that we didn't lose any of our insulators to the river. It was hard enough to fish them out of the floods again, but this time we had learned our lesson and distributed our load evenly throughout the dinghy. The haversack containing our provisions and the rifle had also taken a good dunking in the water.

We reached the mouth of a small tributary coming from the east—that is, from Finland. If my memory does not deceive me, its source was located at the foot of "my" golden mountain, scarcely thirty kilometers away.

Thirty kilometers was not an enormous distance —after all, we had just that day covered such a stretch with our boat. But we had traveled downstream. The mountain, however, lay thirty kilometers upstream and I had no idea whether the tributary was navigable, seeing that it was quite narrow at the point where it flowed into the mainstream. I decided to ask our host, the fisherman.

Early that morning I sent Kurt ahead to the boat, lingering a while longer myself, pretending that I wanted to wangle a few more eggs and butter from our fisherman. It was my good luck that the old man spoke Norwegian; we could communicate well with each other. When I told him that I wanted to visit the Finnish mountain, he looked at me in a most peculiar way.

"That's not a good idea," he commented calmly.

My old suspicions came to the fore again. Could the old man be in contact with the resistance fighters?

"Why not? My passion is mountain climbing and besides, when the war is over, I intend to study geology. For me, any isolated mountain in the middle of the jungle is something remarkable, worthy of exploration."

The fisherman bent over to me. "There's something wrong with that mountain," he whispered in a secretive manner. "People say the place is haunted. I remember when I was a young man that some men tried to climb that peak, but when they returned their minds were all confused. No, give up that notion! That mountain is hexed."

"But it would be possible to get to the foot of the mountain by boat?"

"You need a motorboat for that. Or you could go on foot. The forest stops very soon."

I thanked him and joined Kurt, who was already sitting in the bow of the dinghy waiting for me. He watched me with a look of satisfaction as I stashed the eggs away in our haversack. We pushed off and floated on downstream to the Tanaelv.

We had another twenty kilometers to cover before reaching our destination.

Kurt wanted to make another stopover for the night, but I was most anxious not to waste any time. I had already figured out how we were to get back to Karasjok, and my entire plan was based on that. I tried to put him off by promising that I was just as interested as he in taking a day off—but not until we'd safely delivered our insulators. Kurt agreed to that without much urging.

To take one day's furlough without official permission meant desertion, according to the strict rules of the German Wehrmacht. Nobody must find out about this, although I firmly believed my major would turn a blind eye if I'd report to him about this romantic impulse.

In any case, it was only noon when we landed on the sand bank, our destination—which I already knew

from having seen it before from the air. We dragged
the heavily laden boat through a shallow water chan-
nel, and breathed a sigh of relief as we reached the
deeper tributary and were once again able to use our
paddles. After a few hundred meters through an almost
impenetrable jungle—exactly what I imagined a cruise
down the Amazon River would be like—the river widened to become a small lake.

We had arrived.

The platoon leader greeted us as if we were his
long-lost brothers, and immediately gave the order to
unload our vessel. His men had finished setting up
the telegraph masts—tree trunks felled and worked up
to poles right on the spot—and had also strung the
wires. All that was needed now were the insulators,
so that their work could proceed. We were instructed
what to do next, and returned to the sand bank and
our rubber boat. We let out the air, dried it out, and
folded it up. Then we gathered some dry wood, lit
a huge fire—and waited.

Hardly an hour later, we heard the sound of an
outboard motor approaching from upriver. The noise
became louder and louder, and soon we saw a Lapp-
lander boat with one occupant round the bend of the
Tanaelv. The boat headed straight for the sand bank
and landed, its keel grinding to a stop on the sand.
The engine died down.

A young Norwegian jumped ashore and walked
toward us. "We can leave right away," he called in
German.

Everything seemed to have been organized perfectly. I hoped that things would work out with him;
otherwise all my well-prepared plans would come to
naught.

We welcomed him and stowed our rubber dinghy
in his motorboat. Off we went, but this time upriver
and twice as fast as before, when paddling our clumsy
rubber dinghy downstream. Since we started out fairly
late in the afternoon, it was evening when we reached
the mouth of the river where the old fisherman dwelt
all alone in his hut.

Without consulting us, our captain steered toward the small bay and landed on the shore, close to the old fisherman's hut.

"We'll stay here overnight," the Norwegian announced.

We certainly had no objections.

While our guide greeted the old fisherman, quickly arranging what to pay for one night's lodging in the hayloft—such details seemed to be part of the Norwegian's duties and included in his fee—Kurt turned to me and said: "I wonder if we could talk him into staying here for a day? I'd like to go fishing with the old man. I've always been crazy about fishing."

Kurt had no idea how much his desire coincided with my own wishes.

"I guess so. I've a bottle of aquavit in my baggage, and for that brandy he would be willing to sell his own wife. Just let me take care of everything. You'll see, we'll get our day's leave after all. Besides, we already have a headstart of two days over the first two boats."

Whether we went fishing or climbed a mountain, in either case it represented an unauthorized absence from our troop. Kurt had me just as little in his clutches as I had him. That was important.

After dinner around an open fire, I took our guide aside. I gave him the bottle with the rare stuff.

"Listen, Jörn. I want you to develop some engine trouble so we have to stay here tomorrow. You repair the damage, and then go on a little trial run to see that the motor is working all right again. I'll accompany you on that little trip. We'll go up that tributary."

He looked at me with uncomprehending eyes, all the while holding the bottle in the crook of his arm like a mother cradling her beloved baby. "But the motor is in perfect working order . . ."

"So much the better, Jörn. Then we run no risks at all. You know that mountain over in the east, over there in Finland. I'm interested . . ."

"The devil's mountain?" Jörn clutched his bottle as if he feared I might take it away from him again.

"It haunted. Nobody dares go near the place."

"How close can we get to it if we go by boat? Do you know?"

"Sure. I've been that way many times to go hunting. The river is navigable for about twenty kilometers, no more. After that there are waterfalls, or reefs, or else it is too shallow. But the devil's mountain is only five kilometers away. You can see it from there." He looked at me urgently. "What do you want there?"

"To see the mountain, that's all."

"All right then, it's a deal. But nobody must ever find out about it, or else I won't get my money. I'll be in trouble."

"Our troubles would be far worse," I assured him. He needed more than a bottle of schnapps to make quite sure, I realized. "It'd be off with our heads for us—just for one day of going AWOL."

We returned to the dying fire. The final words exchanged between Kurt and the old fisherman reassured me that those two had also come to an agreement.

The sun was shining right into our eyes when Jörn and I started the boat engine the following morning. We were steering east and upstream along the small tributary of the Tanaelv. This small river was much narrower than the mainstream, but seemed to be deeper. It had no name, Jörn told me. Toward noon I saw the mountain rising up ahead of us, with its white, glistening, rounded top—bare slopes devoid of any vegetation except for the first hundred meters at its foot.

Shortly before reaching a roaring rapid in the river, Jörn made for the shore.

"It's just five kilometers from here. Do you really want to go there?"

"I'll be back by evening. Have a good time till then."

He pointed to his bottle. He seemed to have taken a few good swigs from it already. "Don't worry about me. I'll have a great afternoon with my aquavit."

We said good-bye, and I knew that he would wait

here for me—even if I stayed away for three days. I could completely rely on him.

I had left the rifle with Kurt. If there was actually a group of resistance fighters who had their base on this mountain, it would be better if they found me unarmed. I took along two small cans of meat and a hunk of bread. I would find water without any trouble in this area. Of course, I had not forgotten to stuff a small supply of cigarettes and matches in my pocket.

The dense vegetation in the surrounding woods soon cleared, and I made good progress. I had marched for nearly an hour, when the terrain grew considerably steeper. I had reached the lower part of the mountain, whose rounded peak still towered some 300 meters above.

A while later I found a path. It meandered uphill in wide loops, not at all too steep and strenuous but rather restful, as if intended for vacationers out on a hike. I followed the winding road for a quarter of an hour, then stopped and looked back. Down below I saw the forest stretching toward the west. Farther over to the north, I recognized the river where Jörn was waiting for me. The Tanaelv itself was not visible.

Quite leisurely, I proceeded to open one of the cans of meat, cut off a slice of bread from the big hunk I had brought along, and enjoy my repast. I felt no fear, maybe because the sun was shining and would not really set for several weeks. Moreover, I was not plagued by any feelings of apprehension. If this strange mountain should really turn out to be a hideout for my secret friends, and they should nab me, I could tell them enough names to insure my immediate release.

I shoved the empty can under a rock, lit a cigarette, and marched on. Not much farther now till I would reach the snow-line. The thought of snow struck me as peculiar, since I was perspiring heavily. Such contrasts were something one had to get used to in these latitudes, north of the arctic circle.

The ground turned moist as soon as I noticed the first thin threads of melted snow trickle downhill. The path itself remained free of snow until I came within fifty meters of the top of the mountain. Very abruptly, the zone of eternal snow began—right in front of me. I came to a halt, for what seemed so odd that I have been unable to ever forget it even to this very day, some twenty-eight years later.

The path came to an end before a white wall, five meters high. The wall stretched to the right and left and circled the mountain's peak like an artificial bulwark. I felt as if winter started just ten meters ahead, while I was still standing in plain summer weather. The snow wall looked as if it had been cut with a milling machine.

Impossible, surely, that it could ever have formed this way by itself!

While I was still pondering over this phenomenon, I became aware of movement higher up in the snow. My eyes had adjusted to the blinding brightness, and I was able to distinguish fairly well a white-clad figure against the white background of the hilltop. I assumed this white garment to be a camouflage suit, and the man inside to be a Norwegian, of course. So I called out in Norwegian to him: "Hello!"

The man did not reply. He stopped and looked down at me from about twenty meters away. He impressed me as strangely cool and imperturbable, as if all he needed to eliminate me was a tiny flick of his fingers. I still felt no fear, though I was not exactly in a laughing mood. I kept thinking of the Norwegians who called this area "the devil's mountain."

"May I come up and join you?" I asked, this time rather loudly to make quite sure he would hear me. But once again he did not respond to my question. He simply kept looking down at me as if I were a bothersome insect he contemplated squashing with his shoe. I did not dare continue on my way without first having obtained his permission.

So I tried once more: "I'd like to climb all the way up to the top of this mountain. Do you understand me? I'm a mountain climber."

He answered without resorting to speech, but his gesture was plain enough. He shook his head twice, very energetically, then raised his right arm and pointed down toward the plain. With that he turned around, paying no further attention to me, and a moment later vanished from sight.

I had been unable to observe where he disappeared to. The snow beyond the wall offered me little chance of taking cover, none at all in fact. And yet it seemed as if the snow had simply swallowed up the stranger.

This is when I began to experience fear for the first time. Whether these people were resistance fighters or something else, they were definitely not amicably inclined toward me. They did not want me to join them and learn their secret. It was fortunate for me that they did not know that I'd already discovered it while flying over this area, although I still had no idea what the secret was. I was not in danger. They simply had taken me for a harmless fool who wanted to climb a mountain.

I turned around and retraced my steps.

When I got back to the river, Jörn was sitting near the boat, fishing. He was obviously relieved to see me return safe and sound. He put his fishing rod on the ground and walked toward me. Judging by his gait, not much could have remained in the bottle of aquavit.

"Did you get all the way to the top?" he wanted to know.

"Just as far as the snow line, Jörn. I couldn't make it any higher."

He gave me a knowing nod. "Sure. It's much too cold up there." And then he asked: "Didn't you see the snowman?"

I stared at him. Could he be talking about the man in white?

"Snowman? What do you mean?"

An embarrassed grin came over his face. "You know, people tell funny stories. They say a snowman has lived on that mountain for centuries. My grandfa-

ther saw him once, when he was searching for gold up
there. I'm sure you're aware that there is gold in these
rivers. Grandpa didn't think that was enough. He
wanted to discover the gold vein that would make him
a rich man. So he climbed that mountain, but the
snowman drove him back. That was more than forty
years ago."

Forty years ago! There was no German army
here then, no war, and no resistance movement either!

So who could this snowman be that I had just
seen with my own eyes?

"Let's get back to the base! On the way back
you can tell me more about that mountain."

Unfortunately, there was no more information I
could squeeze out of Jörn than he had already told
me. His grandfather had seen the snowman—that was
all he knew. My description of the snowman seemed
to coincide with what his grandfather remembered. So
forty years ago my snowman must have looked exactly
the way he did today.

The following day Jörn brought us back to Karasjok. We called local headquarters, and two hours later
we were picked up by an army truck.

The commanding officer praised us for delivering
the insulators so promptly by water.

I was looking for another opportunity to turn up,
and this time I planned to take along my carbine.
Unfortunately, I had to accompany my major for several weeks, when we had to be constantly on the move.
When we got back to the base, the telegraph lines had
been completed. No more supply trips were needed.

I decided I would make my own opportunity.

How could I guess that it would take twenty-
eight years?

* * *

Helmut crossed the border and drove to Kemi,
a Finnish city located at the mouth of the river Kemi-
joki on the Gulf of Bothnia. Here began the Arctic
Sea road which went all the way up to Kirkenes.

Three days later we made a stopover in Ivalo. This town lies somewhat south of Lake Inari, about 150 kilometers distant from my "devil's mountain." Near Ivalo, the road to Utsjoki and Polmak branched off to the left—the only road if we wanted to get to the Tanaelv River. I had no choice but to tell Helmut the secret. I had no other way to explain why we should suddenly use a side road for the final stretch to the Arctic Sea.

He was enough of a gentleman not to laugh in my face. Nevertheless, he sounded skeptical. "Did you check the map? Are you sure we'll pass by that mountain? When you were here, there weren't any roads."

"Not if you started out from the Tanaelv River, but they had roads coming from the Finnish side. I suppose they're asphalted by now."

"Let's hope so. We have only two spare tires!"

I looked at him expectantly. "We're driving up to Utsjoki then?"

"Why, of course. I want a look at your snowman!"

Twenty-eight years ago, the whole story made no sense—especially the fact that the mysterious man in white had been observed forty years earlier and was supposed to have lived for centuries on top of the only mountain in the area. By now, however, matters had assumed quite a different aspect for me, even if I could not tell Helmut about it. He had no inkling of what I had experienced in the meantime, although he was familiar with Erich von X.'s two books.

I was very confident I had discovered the control base of the Altairians. At the very least, it was one of their minor branches for the extreme north, and it had been operating there for a long time. If the aliens' activities had given rise to legends long ago in the days of antiquity, why shouldn't they still be occurring in our own age? Moreover, the Lapplanders had a reputation for being superstitious, but they were not liars.

We passed through the little town of Inari, leaving

Lake Inari over to our right. The lake was so big that we could not make out the opposite shore.

We spent the night in Karigasniemi. I felt strongly the sensation that I had returned to an old, almost forgotten homeland.

The sun was shining bright in a clear-blue sky when Helmut started the car the following morning, and we set out on our way in the direction of Utsjoki. The terrain rose imperceptibly, and became drier. There were fewer swamps now over to the right side of the road. They gave way to hills, and even occasional clumps of bushes and trees.

I never stopped comparing the countryside with my road map. There were few landmarks to establish our location. The mountain was supposed to be ahead of us to the left, but I could not see any sign of it. The mountain had no name on the map. No mention was made of its altitude.

When our side road merged with the direct connecting road from Kaamanen to Utsjoki, I finally caught sight of the mountain.

"It's just twelve kilometers from here," I said to Helmut. "Maybe we can get closer, so we could save ourselves that long hike on foot. The terrain doesn't look too bad."

"Yes, and the ground seems fairly dry. Let's drive on slowly. If you see a path, let me know."

A low-lying range of hills gradually vanished from our field of vision. Lonely, majestically, our mountain rose from the surrounding plain, its rounded peak covered with snow, just the way I had remembered it all these many years. The past was coming alive again. I couldn't help feeling that any moment now one of the gray military trucks would show up, as they had been all over Europe during the Second World War.

A weed-overgrown ditch ran along on our left, not very deep. If necessary we could drive our VW bus over it. But the countryside beyond did not look any too inviting. Birch trees with trunks as thick as a man's arm grew all over, sometimes not more than one

or two meters apart. We would have needed a hatchet
to chop a path to get through. Despite our enthusiasm
for this adventure, we felt no desire to do that. Even
the Lapplanders were in need of firewood and building
timber; it stood to reason that we would somewhere
come upon a possibility to drive our vehicle into the
brush.

What we suspected turned out to be really the
case.

"Stop the car!" I called out to Helmut after we
had rambled along the uneven ground for nearly ten
minutes. "That looks like a road over there."

It not only looked that way; it actually was pass-
able for an automobile. Our car rattled across the shallow ditch, and then we stopped the car and shut off
the engine.

There were two ruts in the road which might have
been made by either reindeer carts or automobiles.
They were not especially deep, and there was no danger of getting stuck or throwing a rod. The two ruts ran
fairly straight, and directly toward the mountain.

We walked down the road for half a kilometer,
without noticing any worsening of its condition. Helmut
stopped.

"Let's give it a try, Walter. If we drive carefully,
nothing much can happen to us. And even if we
should get stuck somewhere along the way, the two
of us can get the car going again."

We marched back to our VW bus. Helmut started
the motor, and then we began to move toward the
wilderness. I thought we had suddenly been transported
into the African veldt. We had to shut our windows to
keep out the swarms of flies that abounded in this
dry steppe, making life miserable for the unwary.
That plague would cease as soon as we reached the
mountain, I remembered.

But we weren't there yet.

We covered ten kilometers in our vehicle. More
than once we found side roads which branched off to
the right and left. But we did not deviate from our

path. We headed straight for the mountain, whose glittering snowcap seemed to draw us nearer in a magical way.

Then the road ended, at a man-made clearing on the banks of a brook.

We were about five kilometers from the mountain. It was 11 o'clock.

I climbed out of the bus and stretched my weary bones. Helmut followed suit. He pushed up his arms with a violent, jerking motion, as if he wanted to pluck the sun out of the sky—and then it happened.

He suddenly screamed as if he had been bitten by a snake, then collapsed with a groan. At first I didn't realize what had happened, and gazed at him, all confused.

"What's the matter? Did you hurt yourself?"

He looked up and grimaced with pain.

"That damned slipped disc of mine! I should have remembered it! Now I'll have such pain in my back for the next few days that I won't be able to drive or to sleep!"

I had suffered often enough from my own lower back to sympathize. All it takes is to forget for a moment and to indulge yourself in a good stretch, and suddenly you're flat on your back for days. You think you're halfway paralyzed and will have to walk on crutches. In the good old days people believed a witch had put a hex on you.

I looked up at the mountaintop—it, too, was supposed to be hexed.

"That'll mean the end of our hike, I guess," I said, and sat down next to my friend. "You can't climb a mountain in such a condition. Why don't you stretch out for a while and rest your back."

He shook his head.

"That would be the worst thing I could do. I wouldn't be able to get up again. I'll just stay here. Later I'll try to stand up and walk around. It'll take some time, but it gets gradually better. It's old age creeping up on us!" He managed a wry grin. "Don't waste any time, Walter; get going. I'll stay here and keep an eye on the car."

"But I can't leave you by yourself," I protested —while I was having a hard time concealing my joy at this fortunate turn of events, which would permit me to be alone in exploring the mountain peak. He was a nice guy, my friend Helmut, always so obliging! "If something should happen to you . . ."

"What do you think could happen to me here? Nothing! Besides, I must confess now that I'm too lazy to climb up this mountain. Get going. Hurry up, before winter comes."

My provisions were stashed away in one of the handy haversacks which I fastened to the belt of my blue jeans. A loaded derringer—small and inconspicuous—was hidden in my right trouser pocket. I hoped I would never have to use it, but it gave me a sense of security.

We shook hands. I crossed the brook, waved back once more to Helmut, then followed the narrow footpath which led in the exact direction I desired.

I don't remember what I actually expected would happen, but I certainly had no idea what a fantastic encounter was awaiting me on my magic mountaintop.

* * *

The footpath did not lead to the summit, but lost itself in a rock-strewn slope close to the mountain base. I had to find another path.

There were hardly any rocks up this side of the mountain. Its lower part, covered by earth and grown over with clumps of grass, provided sufficient foothold to try climbing upward without a road. The main point was to gain as much altitude as possible. The sun's rays now slanted from the left and did not blind me. It was no longer as hot as before, since a cool breeze wafted in from the north. Also the buzzing and stinging swarms of flies had ceased to pester me.

Now and then I would glance back, but I could not see Helmut and the car. And gradually I stopped worrying about them. My thoughts were preoccupied with the main task. I was here to fulfill a real mission. I was struck by the thought that somebody should be walking here beside me who deserved like no one else to participate in this undertaking. And perhaps there should be still another person here, to whom I was indebted for many useful hints. But both men were unable to accompany me on this mission. One had to stay home and tend his patients, while the other was sitting in the penitentiary doing time for crimes he had never committed.

When I reached a height where low brush no longer grew, and only sparse grass was covering the ground, I stumbled on a path which led to the summit in comfortable serpentines.

I followed it without hesitation, after I had smoked a cigarette. I must have overestimated the mountain's relative altitude when long ago I had first sighted it from the airplane. The plain below was situated at least 300 meters above sea level. The mountain itself could not be any higher than 350 meters, which was a considerable elevation, visible from afar in the midst of this rather flat landscape.

I was approaching the snow-line, my curiosity raised to a high pitch, wondering if everything would happen the same as twenty-eight years ago. Then I was forced to stop when I came upon the snow wall. Today, more than ever, I was firmly convinced that this had not been fashioned by nature.

These suspicions were soon to be confirmed.

I rounded the last serpentine. From there on, the path led straight to the unchanged snow wall, rising five meters above the ground. I hesitated for a moment. Everything looked exactly the same, although this time I had arrived from the opposite direction. The snow wall ringed the mountaintop all around. I was about fifty meters from the wall, which was topped by the glittering, white, dome-shaped summit. Or was this perhaps an artificial cupola?

I slowly advanced toward the snow wall, overcome by a weird sensation. Maybe someone was observing my approach, registering all my movements, keeping me under surveillance—getting ready to give me a hot reception!

Now was the moment when the white-clad strangler would appear, the way he had done for sixty-eight years . . .

Something quite different took place.

The snow wall immediately in front of me began to flicker and waver in a section nearly two meters wide, as if an invisible fire had been lit between myself and the wall. The rising heat set the air in motion. The wavering increased in intensity until the snow beyond appeared totally distorted, so that my eyes were unable to see it any longer. As soon as the wavering air layer became stabilized again, my eyes perceived —instead of the smooth, white wall of snow—a slanted passage, two meters wide, which led up to the summit. The snow remained to the right and left of the passage, whose floor was dry and level and covered with a bluish synthetic material I could not identify.

As inexplicable as all that seemed to me, I had to conclude that it was an unmistakable invitation to continue to the summit. No doubt existed in my mind. Otherwise "they" would not have revealed what was hidden behind this three-dimensional Fata Morgana. It was an unimaginable display of a technically advanced expenditure. "They" were ready to receive me now—whoever "they" might be.

I walked on slowly—a blue sky above; to my right and left the five-meter-high snow walls that did not radiate any cold. I didn't touch them. In these decisive moments I restrained my impatience, lest I should alarm my unknown hosts. It would not be long now till I would finally learn the truth.

I came to the end of the snow walls. When I had left them ten meters behind me, the entire grotesque scenery changed abruptly again. With a single step I crossed over an invisible border, which returned me from an illusionary world back to reality.

What a fantastic reality!

The snow had vanished as if by magic. My eyes

beheld the golden cupola that so long ago I had seen momentarily aglitter in the sky while I flew over the area. The golden dome formed a roof over the mountaintop and blotted out the sky. Below the dome spread a flowering garden, warmed and lit up by the rays of artificial suns, and I felt a comforting warmth pass through my thin pullover.

After moment's hesitation, I continued straight ahead, although many paths kept branching off to the right and left, soon to disappear among the stands of shrubs and trees of the garden. Before me, just below the actual summit, rose a flat-roofed circular pavillion. Columns circled the terrace, supporting the upper part of the structure. Almost like a Greek imitation, I thought, but then I was distracted by the appearance of two men.

They came out of the building and stood on the terrace, arms folded across their chests. They waited for me with all calmness—and with an openly displayed air of superiority.

I stood before them.

They did not wear the white camouflage suits, but were dressed in close-fitting, silver-gray uniforms that lacked any insignia. Under their narrow trouser legs I could see the outlines of short boots. A wide belt circled their waists. Their faces at first suggested some Asiatic race—but then I could no longer see the resemblance. It was difficult to classify the strangers according to racial background. A thin-lipped mouth, a narrow nose with almost transparent, delicate nostrils, and eyes that were straight out of a Chinese picture book: slit-eyed with a definite upward slant! But that was combined with the most incongruous eye color: the purest azure-blue, and sparkling like diamonds! And their hair! I believed for a moment I had returned to my childhood. Their long hair was golden! Like actual threads of gold! Not white-blond—but a deep, golden-yellow color!

We regarded each other without a word. Then one of the men began to smile—and displayed the most gorgeous double row of teeth, which would have caused any pearl manufacturer of this world to grow pale with envy. He advanced toward me, stretched out his hand in greeting and spoke in a sympathetic, disarming and, for me, most comforting manner: "We welcome you here!"

He pointed to his companion.

"This is Xentara. He'll show you around and will explain everything to you. My name is Xeros and I am the commander of this base. It is needless to tell you that we are the special representatives of the Galactic Colonial Council—you are already aware of that. But what you don't know is the fact that we are nearing the X generation. We have just two more letters of your alphabet to go—Y and Z. Then our time here will be up."

I must admit that I was completely bowled over at his moment. All my life I had wished and longed for this event—the first encounter with extraterrestrial intelligences! I had believed in such a possibility and had often been ridiculed because of it. Deep down in the innermost, hidden corner of my heart, I had realized for thirty-five years, by now, that we were not alone on our globe. But now that I saw my assumption confirmed, I was struck dumb. Tears came into my eyes. I am not ashamed to confess to this weakness. I am no superman, who can casually handle an encounter with emissaries from outer space. I'm just a human being who was suddenly confronted by aliens who had the same outer appearance that we did—the very image of the human race—who were far ahead of us in every respect, maybe 100,000 years more advanced than mankind's present development. Intelligent beings to whom we were indebted for 50,000 years of evolution—if Erich von X., Kofol, and I should be proven to have been right all along in our beliefs.

Perhaps we owed these strangers not merely 50,-000 years of evolution, but even our entire existence!

At the same time, however, these aliens had watched indolently while mankind was tearing itself to pieces in internecine wars, decimating our numbers over thousands of years, while our technological progress made undreamed of giant steps ahead, 100 years ago the same as today.

These strangers from other worlds were like gods, sitting enthroned, reigning over all, watching that their mysterious plan—still unfathomable to the human mind—was never crossed. A master plan that spanned 100,000 years . . .

They must know us, for otherwise they would not speak our language.

They must know *me* in particular!

What was it that they did *not* know?

Xeros smiled—smiled like a human being. Then he said: "We'll give you a chance to recover from your strenuous march. Your friend who remained behind with your car is feeling much better already. You'll be able to see him presently. He's already quite sorry that he did not accompany you, but perhaps it's better this way. Please, follow us." Then he added in a lenient tone: "You won't need the weapon you carry in your right pocket."

I followed them into the interior of the pavillion, and I felt ashamed as never before in all my life. On an impulse, I pulled the little derringer out of my jeans pocket and placed it on the low balustrade of the terrace. The weapon glittered in the light of the suns like an artificial diamond.

The interior of the pavillion exuded an air of matter-of-factness and functionality. Completely gone was the romanticism of the artificial garden at the summit. Here technology and supercivilization reigned supreme. Directly before us was the entrance to an elevator. It was not an ordinary elevator, though, merely a rectangular vertical shaft with an exactly fitted metal plate hovering inside—held in position solely by antigravitational forces.

There it was again: the elevator I had seen 23,000 years ago when I had visited the Altairians in Cuzco!

The realization hit me like a shock. Similar origin, same advanced degree of technological development!

I pulled myself together and followed Xeros and Xentara into the elevator, which immediately began to descend. I could not guess how deep we penetrated into the depth of the mountain, but it was probably more than fifty meters.

The hall we entered next seemed painfully clean and brand-new, not as if it had been in existence here for many thousands of years. The floor was made of colorful squares of an unknown synthetic material—so sparkling clean one could have eaten right off it. The walls were covered with a dull, gleaming metal and gave the impression of having left the factory just the day before. If there were doors leading to other rooms, they were undetectable. The vaulted ceiling consisted of a whitish-yellow surface which radiated both light and heat—another artificial sun.

Xeros stopped and placed his hand against the wall.

A narrow vertical gap formed from the floor to a height of two meters. The gap widened slowly and soundlessly until the opening permitted easy passage for a grown man. Xentara beckoned to me. I followed him and Xeros, who had preceded me through the door.

While the sliding wall panel closed behind me, I gazed in fascination at the sight that had now become visible to my eyes. It surpassed all my wildest expectations, and put to shame the boldest fantasies of my colleagues in the field of imaginative literature—as well as anything I had written.

The control center!

From here they kept us under surveillance!

The room was square, each wall roughly fifty meters, practically empty except for a round table in the middle. The table was five meters across, with a circular space in its center. Inside this hollow sat a man, manipulating the various instruments on top of the slowly rotating round-table strip. His chair was movable in all directions, so that he could reach any of the instruments without effort.

The walls of the giant-sized room told me how it

was possible to achieve absolutely reliable control of events on Earth. The room had altogether a wall length of 400 meters. Not a single centimeter was unused. Touching each other sideways or up and down, without any space in between, was a profusion of animated, lively pictures. There were thousands of screens, all of which could be controlled from the round table. Xeros and Xentara left me time to recover from my surprise, but it was impossible to absorb all details. Even a cursory glance convinced me that each screen depicted a different scene, each one coming from various parts of our globe and viewed from every imaginable angle and perspective.

"Not much takes place in this world that we don't know about," said Xentara, while Xeros walked over to the table in the center to talk to the operator. "It used to be that we could manage with just ten to twenty such picture screens, but then their number grew steadily. Today we need ten rooms like this one in order to keep informed."

Ten control rooms: Tens of thousands of screens!

I had to catch my breath. Xentara smiled indulgently. I fought off a feeling of humiliation. This was not the time and place for it. What for? They had been in existence many millennia before us—a fact for which they did not deserve any special credit. Then they had found us, genetically catapulted mankind's ancestors far ahead, and then kept us under surveillance. As far as I could surmise, they had never interfered in man's affairs.

Or had they, after all?

If they had only stepped in occasionally. . . .

"Xeros has requested that you be given a demonstration. This will enable you to understand everything much better. Don't be surprised at anything—just take it as it comes."

The ceiling light grew dimmer. A transparent wall descended from it and came to a halt about half a meter above the floor. Seconds later, a colorful, three-dimensional picture formed on the new wall, giving the impression that a theater stage was suddenly suspended in the middle of the room. It looked so genuine and life-like, that I had to remind myself that this was merely an enlarged reproduction of one of the monitor images.

I saw on it a familiar landscape—the clearing near the brook with Helmut's VW bus. My friend was heating an opened can of food over a wood fire. I could clearly hear the crackling of the flames, and occasionally some choice expletives when my friend would wonder out loud why he of all people had been afflicted with this cursed slipped disc.

Xeros glanced at Xentara, who was standing beside me. Xentara nodded his head.

"And now one more picture. We want you to understand how well we are informed about all that's going on on this planet. We can view everything and everybody at any time. Of course, we don't limit individual freedom. We are no Peeping Toms, spying on your personal, intimate lives. We simply observe mankind, the press, the mass media, and the progress of your technical and moral development. It is our assignment to inform our Galactic Council as soon as the intelligent life on this world has attained level Z."

I interrupted him at this point. "What do you mean by that grade, Z?"

Once more a broad smile came over Xeros' features, beguiling yet reassuring, like a pediatrician magically making fear disappear in his frightened little patients.

"Z is the last letter of your alphabet. Currently, your planet's developmental stage has reached a point between W and X. If you display some tolerance and listen to reason, you can skip over level X and get to classification Y. And from Y to Z is but a small step."

I could not understand a word he was saying.

Xeros read my thoughts. He explained in a friendly manner: "X stands for planetary war with nuclear, biological weapons. You are very close to this stage. Y means interplanetary space travel, and Z the beginning of interstellar space exploration. The moment mankind reaches level Z, we'll report it to the

Galactic Federation. Then, for the first time in twenty-three thousand years, they will allow our spaceships to land on your world."

"Are you saying that a third world war is inevitable?"

"Oh, no," the Altairian calmed my fears. "All depends upon your fellow men. If the nations, races, and various religions learn to show mutual understanding and tolerance for each other, then no third world war will take place. You'll go directly to stage Y, the era of interplanetary space travel. As soon as mankind gains a firm foothold on the planet Mars, the danger of a third world war will vanish. The mass media will carry the events to any jungle, any hut, any desert, any mountain. A world war will become senseless. Don't forget that today's children will be grown up in another twelve years."

"Why in just twelve years?"

"This date has been calculated by our computers for Mars landings on a large scale—provided the current pace of development is not stopped. Mars landings on a smaller scale will take place before 1982, of course."

I had another question on the tip of my tongue, but I did not have to ask it. Xeros shook his head regretfully and continued: "No, my dear friend, we would not interfere. Not even if this planet's inhabitants tore each other to pieces! One criterion by which we judge if a race is mature enough to join the Cosmic League is when they have overcome the twin viruses of chauvinism and religious dogmatism. Ever since the time when we induced artificial mutation in your early ancestors, the power and decision for good and evil has lain evenly anchored within the human heart. Man inherited the forces of goodness and nobility from his kinship with the cosmos, while the forces of evil stem from the bloodthirsty nature of this planet. The decision must come from within yourselves. Barbarism or the cosmos. We influence certain individuals. We test the reaction of the masses when they became exposed to the 'truth' as proclaimed by such 'messengers.' So far, the result has not been too encouraging. However, you with your novels—and your friend Erich von X. with his books—have made valuable contributions to the thinking of the young generation. Have a look for yourself."

And I saw . . .

I saw Erich von X.

He was sitting at a table covered with papers and folders. The room did not resemble a prison cell but rather an office. I knew that he was working in the administration of the penitentiary where he was serving his sentence.

Erich was making out a list. I could even read what he wrote. I could hardly believe my eyes.

"Menu for the week from the 17th to the 23d of August 1970."

Not too surprising, actually! Considering that he was manager of a hotel by profession, planning menus was of course his job. It was easy to imagine that the prison warden would gladly make use of the services of a specialist. Why not? Everyone must work in a prison.

Erich!

It was the first time I had seen him in nearly two years. He had lost weight, despite his menu planning. He appeared restless and nervous. He had no intimation, of course, that he was being observed—so this was not the reason for his mood. Maybe it was caused by his sense of frustration, knowing he had been condemned unjustly, plus not knowing whether he'd have to serve the full term of his sentence.

The three-dimensional picture screen grew dark, while the light of the artificial sun became brighter again. Xeros returned from the control table.

"Now you'll understand everything so much better," he told me. "Come along. We have just one hour's time for a visit."

Xentara and I followed him to the other end of the room, where another door slid aside. It opened into a smaller room, which contained nothing of any technological significance. The wall screens and control instruments were missing. The cold, functional aspect of the first room had given way to an air of exclusive comfort. There was a wide corner couch with a low, glass, kidney-shaped coffee table, and also some cozy contour chairs made of brown leather. A few bottles and glasses on a tray added to the inviting atmosphere.

One hour, Xeros had told me. Why only one hour? Helmut would, if necessary, spend the night in his car and wait for me. He'd hardly be worried about me at this time of year.

We sat down; Xeros pointed to the bottles. "You'll find here everything you are used to. Help yourself."

I chose whiskey. I needed one. We had a drink and then Xeros continued: "Don't expect any explanations as to why you are now sitting here with us. We have our reasons. Many have climbed this mountain and had to turn back again when they reached the snow wall. Sometimes we even showed ourselves. Superstition is our best ally. The three-dimensional camouflaging image over the summit guarantees us peace and quiet for our work. The rest of what we have to say you can probably guess. Ask questions if you like."

It's difficult for me to describe my frame of mind at that moment. All my life long, I had assumed that mankind was watched over by some higher intelligences. There was evidence in the subconscious of the entire human race, in the teachings of all religions.

Yet now that I found confirmation, it was hard for me to accept the reality. I felt I was dreaming.

I said slowly, "Thirty years ago I flew close to this area. For a second I saw the golden sun-cupola. How was this possible?"

"Under certain circumstances, when several factors are combined, it could happen that our camouflage becomes transparent. A certain angle of refraction of the light, or reflection—in short, sheer accident."

I decided to become more daring. After all, they had invited questions.

"You know Professor Marcel Thomé?" Both nodded. "Then you also know his story—and my own, and that of my friend Erich." Again they nodded silently, as if they had expected this from me. "You must also know of the report Thomé gave me. Is it the full truth? What happened after I returned from the past? After Erich's visit to the Altairian emigrants, did the punitive action of the Galactic Control Council that these illegal settlers so greatly feared—did the annihilation actually take place?"

This time Xentara took charge of answering. "The action was ordered and was executed accordingly. However, to avoid endangering the human race, which at that time had already reached a high level of development, we had to proceed cautiously. Thus it is not surprising that a few of the illegal emigrants escaped destruction. They fled to all the continents. If we had carried out this mission more ruthlessly, the traces would have remained for later generations. So the survivors mingled with the native population—and submerged. They adapted and became true human beings. They became the unknown geniuses that made sure that mallets and wooden clubs were replaced by spears as well as bows and arrows. They brought fire into the other parts of the world. They discovered the wheel. In short, they exerted a decisive influence on mankind's technological and cultural development, without our being able to prevent them from doing so. So, in that respect, Thomé's conclusions were correct. But he was wrong when he assumed that these survivors became the gods of a later day. The memories concerning these early Altairians reach back too far. At that epoch, more than twenty thousand years ago, there was little contact between the inhabitants of the different continents. No doubt, the wandering tribes of nomads, as well as small roving bands of hunters during the Ice Age, brought reports of the suddenly emerged, alien refugees who possessed such special talents—but this news was soon forgotten again. The recollection of these aliens was found to fade during the millennia and eventually vanish completely. However, ten thousand years afterward, an event took place that we could not prevent. Once again a spaceship with illegal emigrants landed on Earth, the result being another unplanned-for intervention of extraterrestrial intelligences, thus bringing about incalculable consequences. The natural sequence of developmental stages of intelligent life on a relatively untouched planet was seriously disturbed again. Therefore, it had disastrous consequences on the cosmic study of artificially fostered life forms. When the ship's commander did not obey our instructions to leave the forbidden zone, we were forced to destroy the spacecraft."

I raised my hand to interrupt with a question. "That occurred ten thousand years ago? Some memory of such an event should remain."

"No. At that time mankind still remembered a catastrophe that had taken place in this corner of the universe not too long before. Due to natural causes, a small planet was destroyed, which orbited the sun somewhere between Jupiter and Mars. The planet burst and became an asteroid belt. Fragments rained on the Earth, causing gigantic fires and floods. Glowing ashes were raining down for days, and earthquakes shook all parts of this globe. So later, when we annihilated the plunderers' spaceship, your ancestors believed it to be a belated after-effect of the previous holocaust."

"Plunderers?"

"Yes. The spaceship that had illegally invaded the forbidden zone belonged to a group of various nationals allied to the Galactic Federation—but who acted in an independent and lawless manner. They would plunder the helpless inhabitants of those worlds which were not under our surveillance and protection. These plunderers were always searching for valuable raw materials. When their sensitive tracking instruments registered that a planet in this solar system had burst into pieces, they expected to find rich spoils. It is difficult and costly to exploit the inside of an ordinary planet. But when a planet breaks apart, its inner core becomes exposed, cools off, and congeals into fragments. The most valuable of these can be gathered up comparatively easily. This is how the plunderers found their way to this area. They ignored our orders to leave, and consequently had to be annihilated. At least, this is what we assumed at the time. But in fact their spaceship was only damaged. It crash-landed on Earth, in the mountainous area you call the Caucasus. Before our search expedition could reach the area, the survivors fled and escaped detection. We could no longer track them down, although it was not long before we began to notice their activities, especially in Europe. They had managed to save part of their technical equipment and weapons. Horrible battles would have ensued if we had tried to bring them to bay. On the other hand, we realized from experience that without reinforcement they would merge with the surrounding population in due course of time. So we did not bother them anymore, for they could not do much damage any longer. They established several bases, especially on mountaintops and impassable areas, and made contact with the human native population in order to obtain food. They employed advanced technical tricks to overcome the Earthlings. There's no need to tell you the rest of the story. You can guess the result, can't you?" I nodded. He went on: "Yes. The outlaws became the gods, heroes, and monsters of mankind's history."

Xentara fell silent, as if to afford me enough time to digest this truth he had just told me. I had suspected something of the kind, but I was inclined to place the blame on the shoulders of the Altairians from South America. Now the situation was clear. Greek heroes, Roman gods—they had not always been kind to man! Now I knew why.

"I have to ask why you are telling me this? You know that I am a writer. Aren't you afraid I might publish it?"

Xeros smiled. "You couldn't do us any greater favor. Who would believe you? You would become the laughingstock of the ages if you ever suggested that there had never been any real gods."

He paused for a moment before he continued. "As for us, we'll remain on this mountain for another two generations. Then our task will be completed.

One of two things will happen—the same as has always happened on other worlds. Your chances are fifty-fifty. The decision of which path you choose is never made by us. You'll either wipe the human race off the face of this planet through a nuclear war—and all our work will have been in vain—or you'll come to understand that all mankind has descended from one and the same family, that all of you belong together, that the planet Earth is your cradle, but must never become your grave. You have to learn that the entire crew of a ship must work together if they ever wish to reach the shore. And the shore, my dear friend, is the stars. There we are waiting for you to join us, with wide-open arms."

Xeros fell silent. For a while, nobody uttered a word.

My mind whirled. Yet it was all rational and logical. The Altairian crew manning this galactic control base did not run any risk by telling me the truth. Nobody would believe me. Even if an investigation team were to be sent to Lappland, I knew what they would find: nothing. Absolutely nothing! An unnamed mountain with a snow-capped summit. That would be all.

Xentara broke the silence.

"There was a third illegal extraterrestrial intervention. Fortunately, it seems to have had no detectable consequences. At the beginning of this century, in the year 1908, another unauthorized spaceship approached Earth. We warned it in time and requested the commander to identify his craft and his mission. Our request was ignored. We sent a second warning, and informed the commander that we would annihilate his ship. But once more he disregarded our message and proceeded to land. Our energy-ray cannon scored a direct hit when the ship was at a fairly low altitude above the Siberian taiga. This event took place toward the end of the month of July of that year—an event which is still fresh in mankind's memory. We believe these unauthorized arrivals were once again either plunderers or illegal emigrants. However, if they had actually landed on Earth in this era of scientific knowledge, the result would have been quite different from ten or twenty-three thousand years ago. We had no alternative but total annihilation of the spaceship."

I thought of another problem. "A friend of mine believes that you have repeatedly intervened to influence our development for your own purposes. Is that true?"

"Not our purposes. Your own," Xeros corrected, thus admitting that Dr. Kofol was right. "However, we could risk only tiny adjustments, without noticeable consequences. Take the case of the sea battle at Salamis twenty-five hundred years ago. If the Persians had defeated the Greeks, then for a thousand years western civilization would not have come about. Your technological progress would have been retarded. The scientific comprehension and practical exploitation of atomic energy that you have reached today would also have been out of the question. And this is but *one* of the hundreds of potential developments that might have followed a Persian victory." He stopped for a moment, scrutinizing me. "What gave your friend that idea? The seaquake, the storm which wrecked the Persian ships on the seashore?" When I nodded, he smiled. "Just an underwater detonation. Nowadays nothing extraordinary, but at that far-distant epoch, only to be explained as a natural catastrophe. The gods were on the side of the Greeks."

"The false gods," I interjected impulsively. And Xeros agreed.

"Yes, the false gods. The real gods had not been in existence for a long time then. They were dead. They had died physically long before the battle of Salamis."

"As far as I am concerned, today is the day the gods died!" I looked at my watch. "And you'll let me go after hearing all this? You won't detain me, or induce amnesia in me? You do run a risk, after all!"

"Not in the least. Even your friend at the foot of this mountain is going to react with amusement when he hears your story. He won't believe a single word. You have no proof!"

Xentara rose from his seat and left the room. A few minutes later, he returned with a sheaf of papers which he put on the table in front of him. The handwriting looked very familiar.

"You are waiting for a report from your friend Erich von X.," Xeros said. "We are aware of that. Unfortunately, he is not in a position to send you this report, which he wrote in prison. Therefore we tele-copied it for you—on the regular typing paper you would ordinarily use, by the way—and would like to present it to you as a souvenir of your visit. He is on the right track, even if his final conclusions are not always absolutely correct. He knew nothing of the second intervention. His next journey should be under-taken throughout Europe. This is where the majority of traces exist, although unfortunately they have also been most cleverly falsified."

He handed me the manuscript, which I folded and put in my pocket. I would have liked to ask many more questions: What was the aliens' life span? At what intervals were they relieved from their posts? How did they manage this in spite of the modern satel-lite surveillance of our planet? Was Altair really their home?

Not until we again entered the artificial garden at the summit, and Xentara pointed toward the path that led downhill, did I dare ask a final question: "There are some people who have guessed something of the truth. They have always run into difficulties. Who is behind that?"

Xeros stayed behind while Xentara accompanied me to the exit. "Other human beings," he answered. "There are many who live and profit from the faith and the beliefs of their fellowmen. Nobody likes to see his livelihood ruined, and even less to stand by idly as they are swept from power. Truth is a dangerous thing, remember that . . . Over there is the passageway. Farewell—and try to forget some of what you were told."

"I can't forget all my questions!"

"You know enough," said Xentara, and waved farewell.

I walked a few steps, and when I turned around again I could see nothing except the snow wall which sealed the mountaintop from the outside world . . .

It was late in the afternoon when I crossed the brook and awakened Helmut, fast asleep on the car seat. He stared at me for a few seconds as if he had never expected me to return, then yawned and sat up. "Well, did you find anything?"

I stuck my hand in my trouser pocket and pulled it out again, empty-handed. "No, I only lost something. My derringer."

Helmut yawned again. "You can light the fire again and roast some potatoes. Or aren't you hungry?"

"Yes, I'm a bit hungry. How long will we stay here?"

"Till tomorrow," Helmut replied. "Then we'll drive up to Kirkenes. I want to see the Arctic Sea."

I put dry twigs and branches on the still-glowing ashes. As the fire flamed back into life, I looked up to the snow-capped summit, the dwelling place of the false gods.

It was only now, today, that the "true" gods had finally died for me.

eight

By September 1970 I was back again in Salzburg. That day up in Lappland seemed to have been just a dream.

In the evening after I finished my day's work at the typewriter, I used to sit and watch television. But instead of my own TV screen, I would picture in my mind's eye the 2,000 monitor screens, and wonder if Xeros and Xentara were now sitting in front of their huge 3-D wall, watching me. To prove to them that I knew what they were up to, I used to throw an occasional glance up to the empty ceiling and grin, as if the cameras were hidden up there. If anyone had observed me in this foolish activity, they'd certainly have come to the conclusion that I wasn't quite right in the head.

But, by God (which one, I wonder?), everything was true!

I had a long talk with Dr. Kofol, the only one besides me who now knew the full truth. I had written to Erich and given him some hints about my findings. I was sure that he understood me. And by now Erich would be feverishly awaiting the day of his release from prison. There could be no doubt in his mind where he would still have to search for the answer to all our unanswered questions.

And I wanted to accompany him on this mission.

"You can do anything, Walter, except *that!*" my friend Andreas interrupted my reveries. For a moment I had to concentrate to remember what we had just been discussing.

"Write about it? Of course I'll write about it. I planned to do that all along. Why shouldn't I?"

"You'll get yourself—and others—into all kinds of trouble. I'm convinced that the descendants of the plunderers who crash-landed are still aware of their origin. They won't let you reveal their secret."

"They don't exist any more. The real foe lives amongst us. And he is a human being just like you or me: People who are afraid that their toy will be taken away, the faith they have clung to ever since childhood. Possessed by this fear, they totally overlook the fact that it is faith in the future which will determine mankind's fate and not their belief in something thousands of years in the past . . . and which they never knew how to interpret correctly anyhow. Do you understand me?"

"Very well. But the danger is still there."

"I'll risk it."

Andreas Kofol gave up. "Well, go ahead. Write if you must. But you ought to bring the report out in the form of a pseudo-scientific treatise, that the experts can pretend to ignore."

"And become a public laughingstock?" I shook my head and took a cigarette from the wooden box on the coffee table. I heard Andreas's wife, Ilse, bustling about in the kitchen, preparing supper. "No, Andreas. I'll write my report in the form of a novel. Then everybody can believe exactly what he pleases."

"A novel?" Andreas looked at me as if he thought I was mad. "You can't put all this important material into a novel! I consider that absolutely irresponsible of you!"

"But it's far less dangerous. The readers will either be entertained or bored by it—according to their mentality. A few will try to separate fact from fiction to get at the very truth."

"They may, and they may not!" Andreas re-filled my wineglass. "Still, you're right about one thing. A novel is less dangerous. Do you think anyone will publish it?"

"There are lots of people who'd like to read it."

Ilse called us to come to dinner, and we changed our topic of conversation. Later, when we were alone again and reclining in comfortable leather armchairs, enjoying our after-dinner wine and a smoke, I took Erich's report out of my attaché case. I had deliberated for a long time whether I should show it to my friend Andreas. But since I had told him all about my adventure in Lappland, he might as well learn the rest.

"Is this the beginning of your new novel?" he asked.

"No, Andreas. It's actually the end of the story. Erich will wonder how I got hold of this copy. The original of his manuscript is in his cell in the penitentiary, together with the copy he had made for me. In my last letter to him, I told him he didn't have to go to the trouble of smuggling his time-travel report out of prison."

"The poor guy!" Andreas laughed. "He must be wondering if you have gone crazy."

"I don't think so. If he puts two and two together with the hints in my letter, he'll guess what happened. The aliens have simply telecopied his original report. Here it is, Andreas, you can read it. It's only a few pages long."

Andreas picked up the first page of the manuscript and began to read out loud. I knew every word of it, but still I listened as if Erich's words were all new and fresh for me. . . .

Report by Erich von X.

On the 10th of October 1968, Hans Neuner and I were standing on the plain of Nazca trying to overcome our disappointment over the sparse indications that the rocky ground had undergone some artificial, mechanical treatment. We knew the gigantic markings, and the runways, needed to be viewed from the air to be seen properly. Nevertheless, we had expected much more from a direct inspection of the ground terrain. Still, what we saw here was enough to confirm my hypothesis: These landing strips could not have come about by accident.

On the 12th of October I stayed behind in town while Hans visited some ruins near Lima. I had instructed him to spend the next few days doing research and photographing in that area. He was not to worry about where I would be during his absence; I would turn up in due time.

A private plane brought me to Cuzco within less than one hour. I took a taxicab to the fortress of Sacsayhuaman, and from there on walked on foot. I made sure nobody was following me.

I carried no equipment or luggage except for the sphinx and a flashlight. They would have to do for my trip. I intended to stay in the past not more than a day or two in order to see and talk with Professor Thomé. Perhaps I could persuade him to accompany me back into the future—our present time.

All was exactly the way Walter had described. The barrier wall opened, and then I saw the time machine. The wall closed again behind me. To avoid running any risks, I placed the sphinx on the floor next to one of the stone guardians. This way it could not become lost again in the past.

I sat down in the chair and closed the door of the cage. When the lamps lit up, I firmly depressed the lever toward the floor. The secret chamber disappeared. The strange, whirling vapors that Walter had called the mists of time began to envelop me. I descended backward in the time stream. If all my assumptions were correct, I was on my way to meet Professor Thomé, aged by another year and a half since the day he had said farewell to my friend Walter.

I left the time machine, found the passage leading to the oval-shaped central hall, and waited for an

Altairian to come and meet me. There is no need to describe the emotions I felt. Two men had gone through the identical experience before me.

The highly polished glass walls confirmed what I had suspected. Energy rays, laser cutters, and glaze polishers had cut the huge chunks out of the rock wall; antigravity machines had transported them to the outside. What remained behind in the subterranean labyrinth were absolutely even walls, polished as the surfaces of a cut diamond.

The robots came to fetch me.

I was glad to find that nothing seemed changed. After all, it had been a year and a half since the revolt of the labor force was imminent. Had it ever taken place? Had it been put down with the superior technical means of the Altairians? I would soon find out . . .

Outside on the plateau I could see none of the machines which had been described to me in detail by Walter. Neither could I detect any worker robots. However, I did see the square-shaped palace. Its ground-plan reminded me immediately of the sun pyramids.

While we were marching toward the steps leading to the building's portal, I turned around to look back for a moment. There was only one visible entrance remaining to the labyrinth. All the others must have been either camouflaged or closed off. All there was to be seen were smooth rock walls and the plateau in front. How radically different everything looked 23,000 years later!

The Altairian who welcomed me in the courtyard had to be the adjutant, according to Walter's description. He seemed surprised to see me; apparently he had expected another visitor. Still, he could be sure that I had the sphinx, for otherwise I would not be there.

There was no direct means of communication with him. Just like Walter, I had to use sign language. The robots were sent away, and the adjutant took me to the commander, who asked me to take a seat and wait.

Shortly afterward, the door opened again. Professor Thomé entered the room.

For a second he stared at me in perplexity, then his weatherbeaten features brightened, and his eyes lit up with recognition. He ran toward me with arms outstretched. "Man alive! Von X.! Finally . . . finally! You made it here!"

I was overjoyed to see Thomé all hale and hearty. "Thomé! Everything okay?"

The commander interrupted our welcoming with a few incomprehensible words. Thomé smiled and replied in the same tongue, then turned again to me:

"He wants to know who you are. I will act as interpreter." He shook his head with joy, then changed over to the commander's language. I'll render the conversation in its natural sequence. "Commander, this is Erich von X., the man we had expected originally, and who sent his friend instead since he was unable to come in person. I believe he still comes in time."

"How long ago did you expect me?" I inquired.

"Three years ago! Thirty-seven months, to be exact. What's new in our world?"

I briefly told him about my book, how it was written, sold and published, and about its success. I did not conceal the enthusiasm with which it had been received, nor the consternation it had caused in many quarters.

"Did you encounter any difficulties?"

"Yes! The troubles started on this trip. I'm afraid when I get back again I'll have them on my heels like a pack of hounds." Of course I had no idea at that time how right I was with that assumption. "Don't worry. I'll handle it all right."

He talked for a few minutes with the commander while I sat in silence, taking in all the novel installations in my surroundings.

Finally, Thomé addressed me: "The commander desires that I inform you about various things that will be of interest to you. The work on our underground bunkers has been completed. The attack of the liquidation fleet is expected to take place next summer. The spaceships won't be able to arrive here before that date. Nobody thinks they'll give us an ultimatum, but we are prepared for an immediate start of the annihilation action. But we are ready! There *will be* some survivors! Have you read my report?"

I nodded. He continued: "The revolt of the native workers occurred a few weeks after your friend's departure. The robots repelled it. They had been programmed to fight back, but to spare as many human lives as possible. When the rebellion was over, most of the natives peacefully returned to their work, and we completed our fortress in the mountain even faster than originally planned. Now nothing is left for us but to wait."

One question preoccupied me. "Aren't there several Altairian colonies already in existence in various parts of the world? Why doesn't the rest of your group scatter all over? Wouldn't that make it more difficult for the Galactic Federation to find and annihilate you?"

He firmly shook his head. "The rest of all mankind would perish together with us. This plan was considered, but I energetically protested against it—successfully, as you can see. The commander shares my views. It is not his fault that his ancestors came here as illegal emigrants. He regrets that this happened, but it can't be undone. Any attempt to apologize or negotiate with the Galactic Federation would be in vain. Of course, some colonies and settlements have already been established. But they are mostly so insignificant that they might perhaps escape the fleet's attention."

I was reminded of Dr. Kofol's fears. "One of my friends is of the opinion that control stations still exist in our own time."

"I share his opinion, but it's better to ignore this fact. I doubt their existence will ever be noted by anyone."

I stayed until the 15th of October. On the 17th my airplane was supposed to leave for Lima, from where I intended to travel on to Chile and then to Easter Island.

The commander allowed me the use of a glider to survey the area surrounding. On most of my flights I was accompanied by Professor Thomé. I admired the fortifications of the Altairians, as well as their loyalty toward the native population—who, of course, could not comprehend all the events taking place around them. I knew that all these happenings would become engraved in the memory banks of generation after generation. Much later, the vague remembrances would burst forth again from the subconscious to the surface. We owe a debt of gratitude to these ancient, alien travelers for the beautiful and mysterious cultural monuments whose real origin became a bone of contention in the scientific community.

On the evening of the 14th of October, I sat for the last time with Thomé. I tried once more to persuade him to return with me to our present time, even though I realized the attempt would be futile.

As I had expected, he shook his head. "No, my dear friend. This is where I belong, with the Altairians. As superior as they seem to be to us in every respect, they still need my advice. Don't forget, Erich, that for them I am a man from the far future. I come to them from a technologically developed era which is standing on the threshold of space travel."

"You'll stay here, then?"

"It's irrevocable!"

I sighed.

"All right then, I'll return alone. You are still convinced the time machine won't be in existence in another year or two?"

"I'm positive, although there's no proof for it. It's possible that only the receiving station in the past will be destroyed, while the one located in the twentieth century remains unchanged, but no longer useful, since it cannot transport objects or people back into the past. If anyone then dares to travel backward in time, he will become lost in the time stream. I am warning you! Make certain that nobody will be tempted to try out the machine. For all I care, you can dynamite the secret chamber inside the pyramid and blow the whole structure to smithereens before it's too late."

"You still don't know who built the time machine?"

"No, I haven't the faintest clue." He smiled at me. "You are the inquisitive kind, Erich, aren't you?"

"Yes, I have a questioning mind. Because there's nothing much I can do with naive beliefs."

The following day, Professor Thomé accompanied me to the time machine and held out his hand to me. "Good-bye, Erich, my friend. Maybe you'd change your mind and remain here in the past with me if you knew what fate awaits you in your own time . . ."

I was later to find out how justified Thomé had been in that assumption! For that Hitler-like district attorney who knew everything better than I myself, and who constantly advanced new accusations against me, asserted among other things that I had attempted to escape from justice and that he therefore had been forced to issue a warrant for my arrest. This would have made me the first fugitive from justice hiding out in the past via time travel . . .

The door closed, I depressed the lever—and half an hour later I emerged from the ruins under the bright sun of Peru.

That same evening I arrived back in Nazca, where Hans had been worrying where on Earth I might be. We discussed plans for a last excursion for the following day, and then I retired to my hotel room and started to make a first draft of my recent experiences and my newly gained knowledge.

These notes became the beginning of my second book, *Gods from Outer Space*.

* * *

Andreas Kofol put the manuscript back on the coffee table before him. "Now I understand how Erich could write his second book so fast and with such assurance," he stated, draining the rest of the delicious red Burgundy wine from his glass. "This time he really had substantiated evidence in his hands, even if he was not permitted to demonstrate this fact. Erich's knowledge of the past and your contact with the aliens' control station in Lappland—if you combine these factors skillfully and put them together like a jigsaw puzzle, the significance of the so-called One Hundred Thousand Years' Plan becomes clear. Mankind is but a tiny fragment of the galactic panorama."

* * *

I have been sitting for many weeks in my sunny work den, trying to put all these events in order. How vividly I remember that one particular experience in my youth—just as if it had happened only yesterday. But the voice that used to call me out of the dark has become silent now. Too many questions have remained still unsolved.

Why did everything begin on April 14, 1935—of all days?

How did I know all about the Altairians even then, without ever having heard of them? Who gave me the idea to write my first novels about them, as early as 1954?

Who constructed the time machine?

When would the extraterrestrials abandon their control base here on Earth?

Which path would mankind follow? Toward its own destruction, or to the stars—to which we have to return in one way or the other?

One day, I feel certain, these questions, too, would be answered for me.

Lately there have been new newspaper reports about flying-saucer sightings. Under normal circumstances I would have overlooked them. Not this time. All the sightings had taken place in northern Norway, northern Finland, and even in northern Sweden—that meant in Lappland!

Could it be that they had seen the reconnaissance craft of the Galactic Federation—spaceships that had not employed the usual precautions?

How much time has mankind still left?

A multitude of questions, and no definite answers to any of them.

I began to write, and while I was about to type the first sentences, I again sensed Erich's thoughts.

There was a bond between us, quite different from any other ever to unite two human beings in the past: our common knowledge of strange truths—and the questions the truths raised.

The day will come when we two will stand together on a mountaintop in Lapland and pose the last and ultimate questions to our alien visitors. . . .

And I know that at that moment the answers will be given to us.

afterword

Three years have passed since the completion of this manuscript.

On September 13, 1971, Erich von X. left prison; eight days later, he visited me. His second book, GODS FROM OUTER SPACE, had achieved world-wide recognition, and he was already at work on a third. Then he set out again on a journey, and for the first time, mention of the Peruvian grottoes and the Equator surfaced in his works. His incredible narrative, THE GOLD OF THE GODS, moreover diverts mankind's attention from the real crux of the problem: *who* built these grottoes?

He knew. And I know as well.

But, not until the present time, have we had the leisure time to go to Lapland, as we had planned. Erich von X. has completed his fourth book and is now working on his fifth. I sometimes get the impression that *someone* or *something* compels him to hurry. Will all the truth about our mysterious past explode in broad daylight before the hour of the X generation?

I don't know. Erich von X. does not know either. He often told me: "My fifth book will sell like hotcakes. And then perhaps, I'll have time . . ."

Time? Why?

Time to confront the Strangers, to ask them at last all our questions?

And to learn from their mouths that we will never attain the Z generation, because we will always remain the X generation?

In 1974, I began to share Erich's doubts. I should not have persisted in my efforts to get this manuscript published. It anticipates the answers to too many questions—questions which, for the most part, have not yet been asked.

But it's too late. The book is now at press. No one can change anything now.

No one . . . ?

Walter Ernsting
Salzburg, 1974

OUT OF THIS WORLD!

That's the only way to describe Bantam's great series of science-fiction classics. These space-age thrillers are filled with terror, fancy and adventure and written by America's most renowned writers of science fiction. Welcome to outer space and have a good trip!

☐	STAR TREK: THE NEW VOYAGES by Culbreath & Marshak	2719	$1.75
☐	THE MYSTERIOUS ISLAND by Jules Verne	2872	$1.25
☐	ALAS, BABYLON by Pat Frank	2923	$1.75
☐	FANTASTIC VOYAGE by Isaac Asimov	2937	$1.50
☐	A CANTICLE FOR LEBOWITZ by Walter Miller, Jr.	2973	$1.75
☐	THE MARTIAN CHRONICLES by Ray Bradbury	7900	$1.25
☐	HELLSTROM'S HIVE by Frank Herbert	8276	$1.50
☐	DHALGREN by Samuel R. Delany	8554	$1.95
☐	STAR TREK XI by James Blish	8717	$1.75
☐	THE DAY OF THE DRONES by A. M. Lightner	10057	$1.25
☐	THE FARTHEST SHORE by Ursula LeGuin	10131	$1.75
☐	THE TOMBS OF ATUAN by Ursula LeGuin	10132	$1.75
☐	A WIZARD OF EARTHSEA by Ursula LeGuin	10135	$1.75
☐	20,000 LEAGUES UNDER THE SEA by Jules Verne	10325	$1.25

Buy them at your local bookstore or use this handy coupon for ordering:

Bantam Books, Inc., Dept. SF, 414 East Golf Road, Des Plaines, Ill. 60016

Please send me the books I have checked above. I am enclosing $_____ (please add 35¢ to cover postage and handling). Send check or money order —no cash or C.O.D.'s please.

Mr/Mrs/Miss_____

Address_____

City_____State/Zip_____

SF—12/76

Please allow three weeks for delivery. This offer expires 12/77.

OTHER WORLDS OTHER REALITIES

In fact and fiction, these extraordinary books bring the fascinating world of the supernatural down to earth from ancient astronauts and black magic to witchcraft, voodoo and mysticism—these books look at other worlds and examine other realities.

PSYCHIC WORLD

Here are some of the leading books that delve into the world of the occult—that shed light on the powers of prophecy, of reincarnation and of foretelling the future.

Bantam Book Catalog

It lists over a thousand money-saving bestsellers originally priced from $3.75 to $15.00 —bestsellers that are yours now for as little as 60¢ to $2.95!

The catalog gives you a great opportunity to build your own private library at huge savings!

So don't delay any longer—send us your name and address and 25¢ (to help defray postage and handling costs).